PIRATES AND PREDATORS

BOOKS BY THE SAME AUTHOR

Birds of Egypt
Life of a Boy
Birds of Arabia
Kenya Diary 1902-1906

PLATE I

The Roman Eagle in white marble

PIRATES
AND PREDATORS

—————— ★ ——————

THE PIRATICAL AND PREDATORY
HABITS OF BIRDS

BY

COLONEL R. MEINERTZHAGEN
C.B.E., D.S.O.

OLIVER & BOYD

EDINBURGH: TWEEDDALE COURT
LONDON: 39A WELBECK STREET, W.C.I

FIRST PUBLISHED 1959

COPYRIGHT © 1959 R. MEINERTZHAGEN

PRINTED IN GREAT BRITAIN
FOR OLIVER AND BOYD LTD. EDINBURGH
TEXT BY R. & R. CLARK LTD. EDINBURGH
COLOUR PLATES BY PILLANS & WILSON LTD. EDINBURGH
MONOCHROME PLATES BY THE GROUT ENGRAVING CO. LTD., KENT

INTRODUCTION

THE FOLLOWING NOTES on Avian Predators and Pirates include all cases which have come to my personal notice. I have also gleaned much from literature but have no doubt missed a great deal. Many experiences related below have already appeared in my own publications. The book is a contribution, not a monograph.

In most ornithological books, the general diet of predators is given without mention of the manner of hunting. I have paid particular attention to this latter point during the last seventy years and have been fortunate not only in having travelled widely but also in preferring being alone when out, without the encumbrance of a chatterbox. Also when in bush or forest I find that by frequently sitting down and waiting, one sees so much more than when interminably walking.

The name Mottisfont frequently recurs in the following pages. Mottisfont Abbey, where I spent my early life, lies in the Test Valley, immediately north of Romsey.

I have always been interested in the manner in which birds make use of other forms of life ; it is an inexhaustible subject. In the section on Autolycism I have given those most interesting cases which have come to my notice ; a great deal has been published on the subject ; what I have written is a contribution and nothing more.

R. MEINERTZHAGEN

17 Kensington Park Gardens
London W.11

v

ILLUSTRATIONS

COLOUR

MONOCHROME

ix

PART ONE

MAN, PREDATORS AND VERMIN

★

Falconry Terms

MAN, PREDATORS AND VERMIN

GENERAL

BIRDS and beasts of prey do not hunt for sport except in very rare
cases: a fox killing a pheasant is going about his lawful business; an
eagle taking a grouse is doing so to enable him to exist. The larger
cats and all hawks kill in a more humane fashion than does man. There is
very little wounding, and death is usually instantaneous.

Man's desire to kill predatory animals probably survives from the days
when he had to compete with cave bears and sabre-toothed tigers and when
gangs of hairy Neanderthalers would mob the lion with the same noise and
fuss which accompany the mobbing of an owl by tits and thrushes today,
except that Neanderthal man probably threw stones and logs of wood. Today
it is seldom that a gamekeeper can resist shooting any hawk or owl he sees—
the larger and more unusual the bird, the more readily will he shoot. That
type of man probably constitutes the greatest danger and does the greatest
harm to many forms of wild life; and the sportsman with the gamekeeper's
mentality is little better—possibly worse—for he should know better. The
excuse is that objectionable word 'vermin'. Every conceivable form of wild
life which might possibly disturb game is classed as vermin, whereas the most
dangerous disturber of wild life and the greatest vermin of all is man himself.
The sportsman, the egg-collector, the bird-lover, bird-photographer and
bird-watcher are all greater disturbers and destroyers of wild life than any wild
predator, who after all is going about his lawful business—survival. I am not
preaching anti-bloodsport propaganda and I recognise man's right to kill for
food, for science, or to protect his own property; but he has no right to kill
for the love of killing or endeavour to exterminate animals whose lawful
pursuit is killing for food. 'No animal species should be outlawed—in doing
so we greatly overestimate our present level of knowledge' (Rudebeck, *Oikos*,
1950, p. 70).

Disturbance of colonial-breeding birds causes much damage to eggs and

3

young, for ravens, crows and gulls at once step in and rob the unguarded nests. In Greenland I have seen ravens and glaucous gulls arriving from all directions to rob the large colonies of fulmar when parents had been scared away; and in Sutherland I have seen both gulls and ravens ruthlessly robbing guillemots and razorbills after human disturbance.

Civilised man—and the more civilised he is and the more crowded he is the more true it is—has a mind which is always under the stress of fear or anxiety. Wild animals, except for moments of hunting or being hunted, forget their worries, if they ever had any. Hence man is more prone to disease and destroys other forms of life more than do wild animals. Furthermore, wild animals breed from the fittest, keeping the strain true and up to standard. Man just breeds anyhow, without any concern for eugenics. It is not surprising that man is mentally and bodily diseased; what is surprising is that man has survived despite the medical profession.

The senseless killing off of predatory animals, or any bird or beast which might possibly cast an envious eye on a hen pheasant or a fat trout, has little effect on the increase of game stock. Increase in food supply, suitable weather conditions during the nesting season, mild winters, etc., have much more effect on game stock than the presence of a few magpies, jays or hawks. Admittedly certain birds like the carrion crow and some of the larger gulls can do great harm in game countries, but they are well able to look after themselves; hawks, owls, and many other birds commonly seen in a gamekeeper's larder have little or no effect on game birds.

I have experienced an intimate knowledge of an estate in Hampshire of about 4,000 acres where from 1887 to 1900 no 'vermin' beyond rats and crows were allowed to be shot by the three gamekeepers employed. Four miles of the River Test provided more trout, grayling, pike and perch than we could catch. A heronry of some forty pairs, many otters, badgers, foxes, hedgehogs and other 'vermin' were left to their own lawful pursuits.

Our annual bag was about 2,000 pheasants and 700 partridges. After 1900 this estate passed into the hands of yearly tenants, and new keepers were installed, including a water keeper. All vermin were ruthlessly destroyed, including the destruction of four large rookeries, otters and badgers were trapped, foxes were shot, jays, hawks, owls and hedgehogs were destroyed, and on the river the heronry was shot out and every little grebe, water-vole, moorhen and coot was killed on sight. The result was disastrous. Coarse

4

PLATE 2

Verreaux's Eagle

fish got the upper hand, and the indigenous trout disappeared to be replaced by hatchery trout. The stock of partridges went down by over a half.

On another estate in Ross-shire, in combination with a deer forest on Ben Wyvis, with a total acreage of over 30,000, we averaged 300 brace of grouse. In 1920 a single pair of eagles and two pair of ravens bred, with a single pair of merlin and a few sparrowhawk. There was a single den of wild cats; stoats and weasels were scarce. Rats were a scourge on the farm.

Between 1921 and 1935 the keepers had no guns, and the only vermin under sentence of death were gulls nesting on the moor. Up went the 'vermin'. Stoats and weasels increased, down went the rats. By 1924 we had two pair of eagles, seven pair of ravens, a pair of peregrine, three pair of merlin, many sparrowhawks and kestrel and two pairs of buzzard: our average bag of grouse increased to 600 brace, with over 200 white hares. The increase in 'vermin' had no appreciable effect on the ptarmigan.

Pearsall in *Mountains and Moorland* (New Naturalist Series) lists vermin killed in Glen Garry, 1837–40:

Foxes	11	Buzzard	285
Wild cats	198	Honey buzzard	3
Martens and polecats	352	Golden eagle	15
Badgers	67	Sea eagle	27
Otters	48	Osprey	18
Peregrine	98	Goshawks	63
Merlin	78	Red kites	275
Kestrel	462	Harriers	68
Ravens	475	Owls	109

Again from Turner's *Memoirs of a Gamekeeper* (1954) come lists of vermin killed on the Elveden Estate:

	1903–15	1926–52
Hedgehogs	5550	11,143
Jays	769	1,583
Hawks	875	1,001
Jackdaws	170	980
Magpies	8	598
Squirrels	4519	—
Otters	3	—

Vermin denotes a form of life which preys on other life and is the animal counterpart of weeds. In modern use the term 'vermin' is applied almost exclusively to any animal which might destroy game, whereas 'weed' is applied to any plant which might impede the growth of cultivated plants. Both 'vermin' and 'weed' are therefore applied to any form of wild life which destroys or threatens to destroy another form of wild life. Man has defiled the earth ever since he assumed the robe of civilisation.

I am glad to see I am not alone in convicting man of senseless disturbance and destruction. Mountfort in *Portrait of a Wilderness* writes: 'Only modern man contrived to upset the ecological balance of nature; man the destroyer, who now kills not for survival but for pleasure; man the despoiler, who razed forests and polluted rivers; man with his mixture of ignorance and sentimentality, which led him to introduce animals and plants into finely balanced communities where, as often as not, they set off a long and tragic chain of unforeseen reactions.'

MAN

*The prime predator and the
vilest vermin*

Surely man is both vermin and weed—not a nice thought; but then man is not nice. 'So unwilling is man to face the fact that he himself is by far the most destructive creature on earth, that almost any other explanation, however fantastic, for the disappearance of that which he professes to wish to preserve is preferred to blaming himself.'

It is all the more remarkable that man has got where he is, a huge devouring weed encompassing the earth, when one considers he can neither kick, bite, nor scratch, is slower on his legs than any other terrestrial mammal, has no natural covering for warmth and cannot even climb trees without artificial aid, except in the clumsiest fashion; all these defects being compensated by craft and cunning—what we now term scientific achievement.

Man's stupidity and lack of knowledge are often responsible for the destruction of predators on the assumption that the prey will automatically increase; it has been shown in Florida that the protection of pelicans has resulted in an increase in fish (*Nat. Geograph. Mag.*, Nov. 1954); and the slaughter of pelicans in Turkey has resulted in overpopulation of small carp with delayed development and failure to attain full size. And so it goes on throughout the world: any predator which might interfere with man is ruthlessly slaughtered, often without adequate enquiry.

I know of no study which is so unutterably saddening as that of the evolution of humanity, as it is set forth in the annals of history. Out of the darkness of prehistoric ages man emerges with the marks of his lowly origin strong upon him. He is a brute, only more intelligent than the other brutes, a blind prey to impulses, which as often as not lead him to destruction; a victim to endless illusions, which make his mental existence a terror and a burden, and fill his physical life with barren toil and battle. He attains a certain degree of physical comfort, and develops a more or less workable theory of life . . . and then for thousands and thousands of years, struggles, with varying fortunes, attended by infinite wickedness, bloodshed, and misery, to maintain himself at this point against the greed and ambition of his fellow men. He makes a point of killing and otherwise persecuting all those who first try to get him to move on; and when he has moved on a step, foolishly confers post-mortem deification on his victims. . . . And the best men of the best epochs are simply those who make the fewest blunders and commit the fewest sins.

Thomas Huxley, quoted from *Apes, Angels and Victorians*, by Irvine.

Food preferences

Most predators which kill, as opposed to carrion eaters, have food preferences, sometimes very marked and sometimes not very apparent. Among mammals we find cattle-killing and sambhur-killing tigers, pig-killing and dog-killing leopards; some lion will regularly kill impala, others zebra; and of course we have the occasional man-eater. My experience of the sparrow-hawks and goshawks is that they have their own particular food and their own technique in obtaining it; I also believe the golden eagle may be a hare catcher or a grouse and ptarmigan catcher by preference. It is the same with many falcons I have watched. I have seen a hobby in Ladak day after day catching members of the swallow family, though other small birds were available. In Britain I believe some peregrines specialise in jackdaws and gulls, while others prefer the duck family. Certainly trained hawks can be 'entered' to a special game requiring a special technique.

I have sometimes noted a moment of uncertainty when a hawk commences his attack: he will start and suddenly stop for no apparent reason; maybe this is because the intended victim is not his especial favourite.

I have had particularly good opportunities of observing goshawk in Germany, Estonia and Britain. Of a single pair in Estonia, one invariably practised still hunting, while its mate, the cock, invariably hunted by rapid low approach and grab. In Sussex I observed the male invariably hunted woodpigeon among beech, while the hen, though occasionally hunting pigeon, preferred pheasants.

The hoopoe (*Upupa*) has a particular attraction for falcons of several species; on many occasions I have seen falcons turn aside on seeing a hoopoe, though other prey was in view. But the hoopoe in his own country can more than hold his own and once airborne is seldom caught.

On the other hand, I have never seen a falcon even attempt to hunt the hoopoe-lark (*Alaemon*), an open-country desert species but with particularly buoyant and strong flight. Not only is the species ignored by both falcons and harriers but the bird itself is utterly indifferent to the presence of hawks and pays no heed.

Individual characteristics

Anyone who has kept hawks knows that individuals of the same species differ enormously, some being timid, others courageous, some sulky or lazy and giving up the chase, others persistent and continuing until exhausted; some prefer still hunting, others prefer a rush and scramble; I have noted among the true falcons, especially in the lanner, that some will gain height and stoop while others prefer a chase in level flight. This was particularly true of a pair of lanner on Mount Carmel in Palestine, the hen being the chaser and the cock the stooper, even though the food of each was almost entirely meadow pipit.

Rudebeck observed 252 hunts by the peregrine, only nineteen of which were successful. I have observed over 200 hunts by peregrine, lanner, the gyrfalcons and merlin, and of these over thirty were successful. An even higher average is attained by trained falcons as the hawk is only unleashed if conditions are favourable.

Regular beats and territories

I can relate a few cases where hawks have had well-defined territories, and regular hunting beats. In Ross-shire, where a pair of eagles bred on the estate, the hunting territory spread over about eight miles from the nest in all directions. I had many opportunities of watching them winter and summer. A hare-drive in winter was a sure attraction, when they would come to the sound of the guns and recover wounded game. But otherwise these eagles had a regular beat, and I could rely on seeing them if I was at a certain place at a certain time, provided conditions were normal—wind, snow, rain, etc. In Corrie Fiola on Ben Wyvis they would always hunt in the morning in clear weather from 11 a.m. to 2 p.m. In mist and rain they would come lower down and could always be found on the south shoulder of Wyvis, either soaring for grouse or hunting low for hares. With snow on the ground they had a different technique: they would hunt the summit of Wyvis for ptarmigan and hares in the early morning and in the afternoon would come lower down for grouse between 2 and 2.30 p.m. Their roost was near the nest, on the north side of Wyvis, on a low cliff. They would sally out about an hour after sun-up in fine weather and about two hours after sun-up in rain or fog. Both would go together, always starting out west, gain height, have a good look at the weather and prospects, circle round the summit and then commence the day's work. This routine was regular, and by posting myself at the proper place, I could almost rely on seeing them. Hunting is not haphazard but conforms to rule and weather conditions.

Again, when stationed in the Nandi country of Kenya I had a pair of Verreaux's eagles resident near my home. In fact, I was in about the centre of their territory which comprised an area of about 400 square miles. After breeding, the young were chased away, and throughout the year I never saw another eagle in their territory except for a pair of bateleur, which were never interfered with, though they bred within four miles of the Verreaux. Weather was fairly constant throughout the year, brilliant still clear mornings and then about 2 p.m. a terrific thunderstorm and downpour and from 4 p.m. to sunset clear and still again. The technique of these eagles was as regular as the weather. Soon after sunrise the pair would set off east, visit some rocky outcrops for hyrax, then circle north over a patch of forest to other rocks, then pass near my home about 11 a.m., hunt along a rocky ridge, then south to the Nandi escarpment and turn east again to their roosting place, where they would arrive regularly about 1 p.m. There they would remain until about 4 p.m., take an evening flight round, mainly for fun, and go to rest about 6 p.m. Of course, if they killed, there was a slight variation or delay, but it does not take Verreaux long to dispose of a hyrax; sometimes both birds would feed together, but more often killing and feeding was independent. I often tried them with a dead sheep but they never even noticed it, though they would always come to a guineafowl if placed in the open in a lifelike manner. I never saw them take a living guineafowl, but I know they did for there were many tell-tale feathers below the nest.

Again in North Uist I became intimately acquainted with a pair of hen-harrier. Their territory extended for about four miles' radius from their regular roosting place, which was in dry heather on the slope of a hill. Each one of the pair took a different route for hunting, the cock being more punctual than the hen. At a small spinney of willow the cock would pass regularly from north to south at 3 p.m. : and at a spot near the coast, the hen would always pass between 2 and 2.30 p.m. After a fortnight in their territory I could map out fairly accurately their daily routine, which was sometimes, if it had been an unsuccessful day, duplicated in the late afternoon.

On the same island and at the same place were a colony of short-eared owls ; these also had definite hunting-grounds at definite times, quartering fields up and down just above grass level. In one particular field every after-noon at 4 p.m. an owl would appear, whilst others hunted other fields and machar, but always taking the same route at approximately the same time.

For a fortnight in Cornwall I watched a white owl hunting by daylight, always taking approximately the same route and flying but a few feet above the ground, and at approximately the same time of day.

Finally, while staying on a farm in Kenya, I remarked how delightful it was to see a secretary bird from the dining-room. 'Oh', replied my host, 'he's there every day at the same time and his mate hunts every day on the other side of the river.'

Method of killing

Death of the victim is nearly always instantaneous, by grasp and crush ; the falcons alone kill by strike ; but if the victim is not quite dead the back of the neck is dislocated ; otherwise the bill is not used as a killing weapon as it is among the crows, gulls and skuas, who hammer the skull with their bill, though they catch with their feet.

The professionals (hawks and owls) carry food in the feet, hawks sometimes, before landing, transferring to one foot so that the other is free for landing. Very rarely falcons will carry small food short distances in the bill. Owls transfer food to the bill when landing. The amateurs (gulls, skuas, shrikes, etc.) carry food in the bill.

Eagles carry nesting material or nest decoration in the bill but food in the talons, transferring to one foot just previous to landing. Osprey catch with both feet, and when alighting at the nest with food, the latter is transferred to one foot.

Competition in territories

Some groups of hawks have definite territories, almost sporting estates, and these are jealously defended. But this applies to residents only; in their winter quarters there is little territorial aggression unless a visitor is caught poaching on the estate of a resident. I have seen a migrant tawny eagle soundly punished by a pair of bateleur in Somaliland; and the pair of Verreaux's eagle in Nandi, to which I have already referred, though not molesting resident bateleur would attack and see off from their estate any other large eagle.

Though the true eagles are perhaps the most jealous of their territories, the osprey and the harriers appear to be the least jealous and readily poach on each other's territories. But I have seen marsh harrier chase a Montagu's harrier from its territory in the breeding season.

I have seen goshawk pay not the slightest attention to sparrowhawks hunting quite close to their nests, probably because their respective prey are usually quite different.

Kestrels and sparrowhawks breed amicably beside each other, their modes of hunting being entirely different.

I have seen both peregrine and lanner strongly resent both harrier and buzzard in their hunting area, though kestrel and buzzard will nest and hunt in the same area without apparent competition.

The most tolerant are the communal-breeding falcons—the lesser kestrel and the red-footed falcon which are almost entirely insectivorous. They do not resent intrusion even close to their breeding colonies.

No killing near nest

Hawks and eagles rarely if ever kill in close proximity to their nest, even under temptation. But once the young are on the wing this self-imposed rule is abandoned. This habit is probably prompted by a desire to prevent

II

drawing attention to the nest. I once found a sparrowhawk nesting in a conifer adjoining a predatory gamekeeper's cottage, the latter being completely unconscious of the fact. If that bird had killed near the nest, discovery would have been almost certain. It is this habit of no killing near the nest which probably prompts prospective victims to nest close to and sometimes adjoining the nests of predators.

This almost sacred rule among birds is grossly violated by gulls who will devour chicks and eggs of their neighbours without compunction.

There is evidence that wild dogs, foxes, leopards and tigers will not kill near their new-born young.

Predators and size of victims

Among mammals, predators will kill animals much over their own weight; tigers will kill oxen, lion will kill zebra, giraffe and eland; stoats and weasels will kill hares and rabbits. But it is unusual for birds to kill prey heavier than themselves, most prey being half or much less than the weight of the killer. But trained falcons will kill birds much heavier than themselves; goshawks can be entered to hares, peregrines to heavy duck and even geese, and other falcons to bustard; Bonelli's eagle and goshawk will tackle gazelle.

Piracy among predators

Piracy among predators is frequent even among smaller Passerines. Starlings have been seen to rob blackbirds of worms (Brian, *Brit. B.*, 1947, p. 340) and blackbirds have been seen robbing thrushes of snails (*Brit. B.*, 1954, p. 47). Among shrikes it is frequent. I have seen in Kenya the lesser grey shrike chase a wheatear until it dropped a beetle, and in Egypt the woodchat will commonly chase small birds in possession of an insect. Moreau (*Ibis*, 1941, p. 614) records the fiscal shrike (*Humeralis*) in Tanganyika as raiding sunbirds' nests and taking the eggs and young of the palm swift: also bullying rollers until they are forced to give up their prey.

Piracy by the skuas and gulls is dealt with under those groups. <

I have frequently seen fulmar petrels attack gulls in possession of food, the gull often being heavier than the pirate. A gull will always give way to a fulmar where food is concerned though the glaucous and Iceland gulls in Greenland prey largely on young fulmar, enjoying immunity from attack.

Nearly all the Raptores will rob each other of food. I have seen a peregrine rob a kestrel in mid-air, the latter being forced to drop the morsel which was caught before reaching the ground. The tawny eagle is a particularly active pirate against his own tribe. But perhaps the record of piracy among Raptores is described by Corbett (*Temple Tiger*, p. 104) when, in the Himalayas, a sparrowhawk caught a bush chat. A red-headed merlin chased and robbed the sparrowhawk, a honey buzzard chased and robbed the merlin, and finally a peregrine falcon chased and robbed the honey buzzard: the falcon then swallowed the chat whole.

I have seen both buzzard and peregrine take a vole from a kestrel in the air; a buzzard rob a stoat of a rabbit; a peregrine stoop at a female sparrowhawk and recover in the air the victim; I witnessed an eagle drive a peregrine from a grouse and fly off with it amid much loud protestation, and in the Sudan I have seen a kite capture a wounded plover in the air, only to be robbed in its turn by a buzzard who had to surrender the victim to a tawny eagle who ate the bird in the air. Large gulls have been seen to rob peregrines of their kill in the air, and eagles, especially *rapax*, have no difficulty in driving falcons from their kill.

Many more instances are given under species.

Recognition of predators

Prospective victims are quick to recognise when a predator is hunting or relaxing. In East Africa I have seen zebra, impala and many other antelope not in the least apprehensive when lion or cheetah are relaxed or just on the move; their behaviour is vastly different when predators are on the hunt. It is the same with birds. I was much struck in Kenya on an early morning when passing through scattered trees where a vast congregation of hawks, mainly buzzard with some fishing eagle and a pair of serpent eagle, were beginning to wake up. The trees were almost leafless and underneath them were several flocks of guineafowl wandering about, secure in the knowledge that none of these hawks were on the hunt. Even when a buzzard would fly from one tree to another, the guineafowl took no notice. I have also seen both grouse and ptarmigan pay no attention to a golden eagle passing over them flying leisurely home with a hare in its talons.

It has been suggested that the releaser stimulus for fear of a predator among birds is the short neck; I doubt that, for many other birds than hawks have

13

short necks. The cuckoo, for instance, has a long neck and is at once mobbed, though small Passerines do not exhibit the same degree of fear for a passing cuckoo as they would for a sparrowhawk. Doves have fairly short necks but cause no apprehension. No, a hawk is at once recognised by birds as a predator; why not? We do.

I believe that every bird knows its own particular predator. Colonies of black-headed gulls pay more attention to a raven or crow than to a buzzard or falcon; terns know their skuas, gannets know their great skua, the hedgerow birds pay scant attention to a kestrel but react at once to a sparrowhawk. Duck sitting on the water pay scant attention to a passing peregrine, though in the air their reaction is instant; they pay not the slightest attention in flight to a harrier or buzzard.

On the shores of Lake Nyasa I watched a large flock of guineafowl go to roost in a big tree, soon followed by a pair of fishing eagles (*vocifer*) who settled on top of the tree within a few feet of the guineafowl who paid not the slightest attention to them. And yet by daylight when the same flock of guineafowl were feeding by the lake shore and the same two eagles passed near them they would scurry away to cover or crouch in the reeds.

Recently in Sweden I saw a large breeding colony of black-headed gulls pay not the slightest attention to an osprey fishing among them; but when a magpie or crow approached the colony, they mobilised for mobbing.

When my family lived at Mottisfont in Hampshire, we had a small starling roost in a patch of overgrown rhododendron near the house; the stench became unbearable and elderberries were being scattered all over the garden from the birds' faeces. My brother and I had two little male sparrowhawks, both entered to starling, but we were forbidden to fly them within a mile of the house; but on this occasion, the ban was lifted and we unleashed our sparrowhawks at dusk into the starlings as they came in to roost. After three consecutive evenings, not a starling came to roost. Would it be possible to clear the Trafalgar Square area of starlings by using a gang of trained hawks for a week or would public opinion rise in indignation?

My house in London abuts on to a seven-acre garden which contains the tallest tree in London. During my 37 years' residence only once has a single cuckoo and a single sparrowhawk visited the garden, each remaining but a few hours in the early morning. The garden contains many blackbirds, single pairs of thrushes and missel-thrushes, a pair of jays, blue tits and many woodpigeon. Very few of these sheltered birds can ever have seen a hawk and yet they all reacted in the same way to both hawk and cuckoo. Birds refuged in thick bushes, the lawns were empty and there was much swearing and cackling even after the predator and mock-predator had gone. The garden did not resume its tranquillity until the evening.

Birds' reaction to predators

The reaction of Passerines to predators is to seek the nearest cover, either tree or bush or rock; but when in flock they bunch; those who scatter are lost. Bunching in tight flocks is a great protection for it is seldom a hawk will risk entering a flock. Anyone who has seen rook-hawking in open country will notice the instant reaction to bunch, the hawk taking the individual outside the bunch. But with the more solitary carrion crow, if caught in the open, he will make for the nearest tree; so strong is this desire to get into cover or into a bunch that I have seen a hunted rook take refuge under a tank on Salisbury Plain or even in a tangle of barbed wire. If no cover is available birds, whether single or in flock, will always endeavour to gain height when a hawk threatens. Hoopoes are particularly successful in this and I have seen a meadow-pipit defeat a lanner by gaining and maintaining height.

Are predators beneficial to the species on which they prey?

Are hawks and owls 'sanitary policemen,' constantly on the look-out for sick birds or the laggards from a flock who for some reason are unable to keep up with the activity of their species? There is no doubt that hawks, and even crows and ravens, are very quick at spotting a 'pricked' bird. And any bird accustomed to the protection of the flock, falls an easy victim to predators without that protection. I believe predators serve a useful purpose in destroying the wounded, diseased and weak, and preserving the physical fitness of their victims. There is little doubt that predators exercise a selective effect in choosing abnormal birds whether in colour, health or some physical or mental weakness. Laggards, a bird which cannot keep up with the flock, tired birds or abnormal in plumage are chosen by predators. It seems therefore that predators are indeed beneficial to their prey and that any species whose physical standard falls below normal, runs the risk of extinction by predators.

15

No small flightless bird occurs except on islands where predators do not exist. The Ratites have only persisted owing to their habitat on open plains, their acuity of vision and their speed. In New Zealand this flightlessness due to absence of predators persists even today. In Mauritius the inept dodo fell an easy prey to human predators, and in many other islands small flightless birds still persist. And everywhere in the world any individual bird whose power of flight does not come up to the standard of its species, runs the risk of capture by a predator.

Physical fitness is the test of survival. I wish that were so in *Homo sapiens*.

During the days of tribal warfare and before the era of world wars, I believe this to have been true of the human race, which deteriorated under long spells of peace but developed renewed vigour in time of war. Peace produced great men in the arts, especially in the art of talking; war produced great leaders and men of action.

Most of the great men in history from Julius Caesar and Hannibal to Marlborough, Napoleon, Wellington and Stalin are those who have contributed to do the greatest amount of killing; it is sad that human history should be made up largely of war, slaughter and bloodshed. It is the predators who have made history and names for themselves.

We talk of peace and learning, and of peace and plenty and of peace and civilisation; but I find that those were not the words which the Muse of History coupled together: That on her lips, the words were—peace and sensuality, peace and selfishness, peace and corruption and peace and death. I found, in brief, that all great nations learned their truth of word and strength and thought in War; that they were nourished in war and wasted in peace; trained by war and betrayed by peace; in a word, they were born in war and expired in peace.

The Crown of Wild Olive

And so it is with birds; without predators they would become as gross, as stupid, as garrulous, as overcrowded and as unhappy as the human race is today.

In wild life there is less suffering than pleasure. Death is usually quick, often painless and very seldom cruel; how very different from the methods of *Homo sapiens* where pleasure is so often derived from cruelty. In the struggle for survival pleasure plays a leading part, so does pain. Both are stimulants to evolution.

16

Though physical fitness is the test of survival among wild animals, the exact opposite is the essence of survival in the human race today where moral and mental attributes are more important than physical fitness. Modern war kills off the best of the nation in both commissioned and non-commissioned ranks and the laggards—conscientious objectors, the medically unfit and those who for one reason or another contrive to avoid fighting—escape, reducing the human race to a soft, diseased, effeminate, and classless society of dear little comrades without incentive and devoid of all the better human qualities, all equally dishonest, equally devoid of tradition, equally ill-mannered but proud of the low position into which they have sunk.

Impact of predatory birds on evolution

In Nature, warfare between species (predators and their victims) leads to evolutionary progress. Without competition and aggression there can only result stagnation and extinction. Consistency is the worst enemy of progress. Are not all recent wars the outcome of competition, which is only another word for overcrowding, and are not competition and overcrowding the main causes of social decadence in the human race?

Love, hunger and need of security are the three stimuli causing adaptation and evolution. If there is no need for security we find decadence reducing birds to flightless condition and often to eventual extinction.

Table manners

Feeding behaviour of communal gluttons like vultures need not be discussed; brawls and grievous injuries are many; little gentlemen like bateleur never indulge in communal feeding though vulturine in habit; but the marabou stork, though a revolting scavenger, soon puts an end to a brawl by true vultures by using his dangerous bill which vultures respect.

It is the table manners of the 'killer' hawks which interest me. I have seen many species of hawks disposing of their prey. It is very rare for a hawk to commence eating before the victim is dead. The true falcons usually do a certain amount of plucking and then commence to feed off neck or breast. I have watched several species of goshawk and sparrowhawk, buzzard, eagle, harrier and kites feeding and what impressed me most was individual taste in handling a meal. If the prey is a bird, it is sometimes half plucked, sometimes

17

(eagles and the gyr-falcons) the primaries are removed; sometimes the head is pulled off first and then the breast eaten; the entrails are sometimes discarded, sometimes swallowed with a disgusting squelch. I have seen harriers start at the breast and on one occasion at the back. Eagles and buzzard almost always do a lot of plucking before feeding; the only occasion on which I saw a goshawk feed was when a hen capercailzie was the victim. There was a lot of plucking of the breast before food was taken and the entrails were untouched.

I have seen a buzzard (*Buteo*) eating a rabbit it had caught; the skin was torn off the shoulder and back before feeding commenced. Nierop (*Bokmakierie*, 1957, p. 39) describes how the small kite (*Elanus*) rips open a mouse, removes the intestines which are cast aside, and then consumes the rest including skin. On the other hand the small sparrowhawk (*Accipiter badius*) makes an incision at the eyes of a mouse, then rolls back the skin and swallows the skinless body.

Bat-killing hawks remove the victim's wings before swallowing the body, skin and all, in the air. Locusts and large moths are swallowed after the wings have been removed.

Hawks who kill snakes and bateleur who find dead snakes invariably leave the head untouched.

I have seen ospreys eating fish on two occasions—near Aden and in Hampshire. Small pieces of flesh are torn from the body but head, vertebrae and tail are not swallowed.

Herding and flocking

The habit of herding or flocking among animals assumes three aspects—aggressive, protective and social. In the following remarks I make no apology for that bugbear of certain ornithologists—anthropomorphism. Some even apologise for introducing a comparison between man's and birds' behaviour as though it were a gross violation of principle and as though stimulus and reflex action were very different in man and wild life.

The herd instinct is not an isolated phenomenon but an extension of individual behaviour; the herd or flock stimulates the discharge of collective energy. The herd instinct has disadvantages. It can lead to extermination. Rinderpest runs like wild-fire through herds and would be less decimating

18

among individuals. Among birds, it is almost certain that the cormorant (*Phalacrocorax perspicillatus*), which nested in vast numbers on Bering Island only, were exterminated by disease. The same applies to the Labrador duck. The gregarious and limited breeding-grounds of the great auk in the breeding season largely contributed to its extermination by human agency. Among humans we find lethal epidemics which must be directly attributed to herding. Disease will decimate the honey-bee. Excessive and unnatural overcrowding, which is an abnormal state of the herd instinct, may lead to decimation—cf. grouse, hares and rabbits, voles, etc.

It has been found that tsetse fly if reduced to very small numbers cannot recover. The remaining few die out and it is unnecessary to kill them off absolutely. Nature finishes them off.

Addo bush and Knysna elephants are at a level beyond which they cannot increase. The reduction to a dangerous minimum probably also accounts for the extinction of the blaubok in South Africa and the near-extinction of the bontebok.

But non-gregarious species such as the hoopoe in Egypt, which was almost extinct before it was protected, recover rapidly; among mammals, such species as the wild cat of Scotland, polecat and marten, recover rapidly.

Birds which flock for migration sometimes meet with disaster owing to weather conditions; quail, white stork, rooks and many others have suffered on migration through being in flock.

The herd instinct may be more than offensive as in the dog and some other predatory animals, or defensive as in the deer, sheep, antelope, etc.; it can serve a definite purpose such as food-finding, desire for companionship, directive guidance on migration or even, as is found among some humans, genuine love of noise and companionship. The latter would appear to apply to the huge roosting 'murmurations' of starlings.

I know of no case where birds concentrate for attack except in defence. That is dealt with under Protection.

But among mammals we find many cases where predators concentrate when hunting—lion, wild dog, wolf. Man has developed the pack of hounds for hunting foxes, deer and hares. The actual physical strength of the pack is a tremendous advance on that of one individual and the same can be said of the senses; two noses are better than one, etc.

The wild dog of Africa and the wolves of northern Europe, though herding for attack, scatter when themselves attacked; their first reaction to danger is dispersal. I have seen wild dogs scatter in confusion when chased by motor car or man on horseback; and both Russians and Estonians have related to me that the immediate reaction to attack on a pack of wolves is dispersal. It is the same with the human race; the mob concentrates for aggression but if faced by soldiery will disperse in an astonishingly short time.

The herd or flock is at a great advantage over a solitary individual.

Herds of wild cattle, sheep, antelope, zebra, donkey and elephant always show comparative relaxation, infecting each individual with a sense of security; this is in marked contrast to the lonely animal who lives in a chronic state of uneasiness and fear; the lonely bull elephant is ever on the alert whilst those in herd relax. The lonely bull wildebeeste or hartebeeste can never relax, whilst when in herd they can go fast asleep.

Whilst sight and smell are used mainly by animals living in open country, chatter is of small importance as each individual can see its own flock; but in bush or forest it is very different; a constant chatter holds the flock together, whether it be bands of monkeys or hunting parties of birds. Forest communities are much noisier than open-country dwellers. There is seldom complete silence in bush or forest whereas in open country, especially in desert, one meets absolute silence. Forest dwellers recognise silence as danger; if a predator is on the move, silence prevails and, whether it be bongo or bulbul, the sudden lack of chatter gives the alarm.

Wild cattle are especially herd-minded when facing danger. The musk ox 'forms square' round the herd; the Indian water buffalo will attack a tiger in close formation and I have seen a large herd of African buffalo concentrate with calves in the centre when threatened by a large pack of wild dog. I have seen it stated that yaks will 'form square' in much the same manner as the musk ox in face of predators; and that zebra will form a line with rumps facing a lion when attacked. But as a lion can with ease leap over the backs of zebra, such a defence requires confirmation.

Herding and flocking has economic advantages and serious disadvantages. A pack of wild dogs eat all they kill; the solitary lion or tiger is most wasteful, sometimes leaving half the kill for carrion-feeders; a large herd of herbivores can do immense harm to crops; the case of locust swarms and huge flocks of grain-eating birds is obvious.

Most birds whose nests and eggs are not camouflaged, are colonial breeders, the flock affording protection through mob-action. The size of bird colonies must be not too large for sustenance of the adults and young, but must be large enough for strength in defence. I have seen tern colonies too small for defence against skuas in Shetland and too large at Pevensey and Blakeney for sustenance.

Small colonies of terns are defenceless against skuas. But if the colony is one hundred birds or more they can hold their own. When laying commences, terns in colony do not appear to mind the intrusion of gulls who will strut about in their midst gobbling early eggs. But when the whole colony is laying and later when hatching commences, tern become more aggressive and resent any intrusion by gulls or skuas.

When watching a large colony of common tern in the Isles of Scilly in 1946—some 200-250 birds—I noticed that there was a posse of some fifteen birds constantly on the alert for raiders. Whether they were non-breeding birds or all males I could not say, but they were taking no part in incubation or feeding and for over two hours the individuals never changed. They rested on a small mound dominating the ternery and on the approach of a gull they would up into the air at once and attack, then return to rest when the raid was beaten off. The rest of the colony went on with their normal business of incubation and feeding. But if a strong raid developed then the posse would scream for help and the whole ternery would take the air and attack. When the raiders were beaten off the posse would at once return to their mound and the rest of the colony continue incubation or feeding. It was a good example of the protective value of herding and showed remarkable organisation. I have observed similar cases of protective posses in colonies of little tern in Egypt and at Sandwich, of Arctic tern in the Shetlands and of sandwich tern in Ross-shire.

Off Noss Head in Shetland at the end of August I came on an enormous pack of cock eider in eclipse. The birds numbered about 224 individuals. They were all flightless and if approached by greater black-backed gulls or skuas they would throw water up with their hind legs after the manner of coot if threatened by a hawk. It was a most effective water barrage made doubly effective by the numbers involved. See also under sea eagle (p. 119) for the coot's defence in 'splash'.

Almost all animals and birds which practise migration, many of whom are more or less solitary in normal life, develop the herd instinct when migratory movement is undertaken. This flocking during migration strengthens security and almost certainly adds accuracy to direction. But it has serious disadvantages. Adverse weather conditions have caused many serious disasters to white stork over the Sahara, rooks in the Atlantic, quail in the Sahara and in the Mediterranean, and to grouse in the North Sea and Solway Firth.

Any soldier will testify to the truth that companionship when in danger decreases fear and that few positions are so uncomfortable as solitude in danger. To be brave in company is a vastly different virtue to courage when alone. Almost all animal life enjoys companionship; the greatest cruelty, greater than the loss of freedom, of keeping wild creatures in zoos, is loss of companionship. The popularity of broadcasting and television is, in most cases, due to a desire for companionship—and noise.

Many species congregate for fun; babblers in Arabia have their evening dance, I have seen choughs in Ushant congregate for a dance, rooks will hold a 'parliament,' blackgame congregate for their concert at the lekking ground whilst the debutantes select their husbands.

Other birds congregate for food, especially game birds—the more scratching, the more food. I believe mixed hunting parties, mainly of tits, benefit from finding food.

Many animals which have developed the herd instinct eat quickly, snatching at food lest a neighbour gets it; such are dogs, pigs, gulls, chickens, pigeons, starlings. Animals devoid of the herd instinct eat leisurely; they do not eat in company with competition. Such are the cat tribe, hawks, owls. Other animals, mainly ruminants and pachyderms, eat leisurely because their food is abundant; but if food is scarce they eat graspingly, jostling each other in competition. I have seen both elephants and rhinoceros guzzling when there was danger of a stronger beast evicting them. Giraffe always feed in peace even off the same tree with nozzles almost touching. The elephant rarely feeds in such close proximity and the evil-tempered rhinoceros never. Horses are slow feeders when food is abundant but will fight well enough if they desire another's food.

I believe communal roosts to be based not so much on security as on desire for companionship in the dark; the noise in a large communal roost surely reflects enjoyment as much as the roar of conversation in a room crowded with sippers of sherry.

'Bunching' in face of attack

Every good soldier knows that concentration in face of attack is a major military principle. The forming square by infantry in face of a cavalry attack, a move which went far to win the battle of Waterloo, is but a form of concentration in face of attack. A flock of frightened sheep will run together for the protection of the flock and I have seen the same manœuvre by many of Africa's big game; it is the well-known musk-ox behaviour in face of attack.

In some birds this defence of 'bunching' when faced by attack is very marked, in others it is poorly developed. In the thrush family there is no attempt to bunch; if a flock of fieldfares or redwing are attacked by a hawk there ensues a *sauve-qui-peut* which ends in disaster. Rooks and jackdaws are good bunchers, the finches bunch but the buntings do not, long-tailed tits will bunch in face of danger but the true tits do not. Meyerriecks (*Wilson Bull.*, 1957, p. 184) describes five unsuccessful attacks on a flock of cedar waxwing (*Bombycilla cedrorum*) by a Cooper's hawk (*Accipiter cooperi*) who was defeated by the very tight bunch; and as soon as the hawk desisted the bunch loosened up. I have seen much the same when a sparrowhawk (*Accipiter nisus*) attacked a flock of snow buntings in South Uist; the buntings formed such a tight little ball that the hawk, despite several attempts to stampede the flock into dispersal or dropping a laggard, had to desist. Starlings understand the protection afforded by bunching in face of attack and so do the small waders and many of the larger ones.

The great skua frequently attacks sea duck, from eider and sheld-duck to the small long-tailed duck. The reaction of duck to attack is to bunch and join a neighbouring party resting on the sea; the skua's technique is to tire out the victim by making him dive time after time until he is completely exhausted. This technique might succeed where one or two duck are concerned but must fail where a whole flock is concerned, for the skua could not possibly keep his eye on one particular bird. This bunching is therefore to the advantage of the duck as it creates confusion.

Mobbing

A mob is a most dangerous assemblage of hysterical souls, utterly irresponsible and ruthless. The larger the mob the greater the danger. Among men, a mob may comprise thousands of perfectly sensible, normal, well-behaved persons, all rendered senseless, abnormal and ill-behaved by some grievance or fear: it is numbers which transform animals into hysterical, abnormal, irresponsible gangsters.

And yet communal breeding, communal roosting, communal migration and communal feeding are, without doubt, a protection and engender a sense of security. Mob tactics are also successful. A snowy owl is known to have been mobbed and killed by Arctic tern (*B. Greenland*, p. 467); a large dog has been evicted at a gallop and with tail well tucked in when attacked by tern; I have seen feathers fly from a raven when attacked by some hundreds of black-headed gulls; I have seen a sparrowhawk after raiding a starling roost drop its victim and several feathers when mobbed by the roost; I have seen house sparrows mob a cat which had caught a fledgeling—their combined action had an instantaneous effect, the victim was dropped and the cat fled. I have seen sand martins mob a cuckoo. Gill (*The Osprey or Fish Hawk*, 1901) records a case of frigate birds (*Fregata*) mobbing and killing an osprey in southern Florida.

The mobbing of predators when at rest seems to me atrocious bad manners. I have seen rollers in Kenya stooping at a harrier eagle perched on a tall tree and compelling him to leave. And how often have we all seen a sleepy brown owl being mobbed by a host of hysterical blackbirds and tits, an expression of outraged dignity and indifference on the face of the owl. Bulbuls have no manners at all if they accidentally find an owl asleep: they will continue their brawl until every vulgar little feathered creature joins in; tits will stop feeding to add their noise to the vulgar scene but tree-creepers and nuthatches refrain. I have yet to see any retaliation on the part of owls. I have even seen blue and long-tailed tits mobbing a hawk-moth caterpillar, doubtless, in their ignorance, assuming it was some poisonous reptile.

Attacks on man by birds in defence of eggs or young are a form of mobbing. The black kite in India has been known to inflict severe injuries on man, ripping open the skin with the hind claw. The brown owl in Britain has inflicted severe injuries on man during the breeding season. The great skua can inflict severe injuries with its bill; low-level attacks by several birds at once can be most painful and even embarrassing; there is a case of a small child being attacked by five skuas on Hoy (Orkney) when away from her parents and only rescued in a battered state and screaming in the heather;

PLATE 3

Tits mobbing a caterpillar

after all, terns can mob and kill a snowy owl, possessing greater natural protection than a child.

Predatory birds have great powers of offence; they are supreme in attack but display little power or means to ward off an attack on themselves; thus we find the peregrine falling an easy prey to the eagle owl though supreme when attacking birds much larger than itself. The snowy owl can kill birds as large as itself but can be mobbed and killed by the combined efforts of a determined ternery.

Peregrines pay little attention to skuas, gulls or ravens who attempt to mob them; the gyr-falcons, heavier birds, are frequently mobbed and driven off or forced to abandon their prey when attacked by large gulls, ravens and even terns.

Usual time of day for hunting

I have seen most hunting either in the early morning when the sun is well up or in the last two hours before sunset. At Khartoum I have seen the many Barbary falcons resting on ledges on the north side of buildings, often lying down on their belly after a morning's hunt, and then hunting again in the late afternoon.

The constant threat of death

Anyone who has watched tits feeding at a bird table, especially if they have to poke their heads into a coconut, is struck by the constant break-off from feeding to have a look round. The same applies to all birds when feeding, whether it be woodpigeons, starlings or the thrush family; they are all apprehensive of attack; it is only where absolute security reigns, as in the pigeons of Trafalgar Square, that there is no apprehension. I should dearly love to unleash six female goshawk in Trafalgar Square and witness the reaction of that mob of tuberculous pigeon. The danger of attack is always present. The whole life of a bird must be constant alertness. If a hawk appears, fear of man disappears. I have seen teal refuse to rise when a peregrine flew hopefully overhead, even though I was but a few yards distant. I have seen one of a covey of grouse when chased by a falcon fly headlong into long heather quite close to me, and half stun itself; I have seen a magpie after being chased by a peregrine take refuge in a small bush and refuse to budge even though a man poked a stick in to dislodge it; I have been within striking distance of a green woodpecker when a hen sparrowhawk settled in the tree above, and he refused to move before the hawk flew off.

On Ben Wyvis in winter I watched a covey of ptarmigan not twenty yards from me on snow; they were crouched low though their heads were turning up and round; looking up, I saw the reason—a prowling eagle; the ptarmigan slowly wriggled close together, all intently watching the eagle and paying no attention to me. That the eagle had seen them was obvious, for the bird suddenly side-slipped losing considerable height; this was possibly a move to induce the ptarmigan to take wing; but the birds remained frozen with eyes glued on the eagle who reluctantly made off. The ptarmigan were clearly more terrified of the eagle than of me.

Though birds in exposed positions invariably evince apprehension of attack by predators, there are occasions when that danger is forgotten in the ecstasies of love song. Most hedgerow birds, the thrush family and others, pour out their love song from a fairly conspicuous position and I believe that during that paean of self-advertisement and pleasures to come, they are utterly unconscious of anything but their own musical effort. I have seen both a cock chaffinch and a cock missel-thrush carried off in mid-song by sparrowhawks before they were aware of danger, so absorbed were they in their own vocal effort. Also, many years ago, I was taken out in Hanover in spring to shoot capercailzie at dawn. After locating a cock 'singing' we stalked the song which lasts for about a short minute, terminating in a fine rattle of pinions. Whilst the song was in progress one could move in full view of the caper, so engrossed was he in his performance; but the moment he was silent he would be off at the slightest hint of danger. Even within fifty paces we could run from one tree to another in the open without being noticed. Ecstasy blinds them to danger.

Attacks on flocks

When a predator attacks a flock he has his eye on a single victim and in all probability that victim is quite aware of the fact, often leaving the flock from fright. Falcons apparently playing with a flock may at any moment select a victim and attack; this frequently occurs when migrant predators feed on migrant waders, pigeon, etc.

PLATE 4

Golden Eagle and Ptarmigan

Behaviour of predators on migration

I must avoid 'always' and 'never.' There is very little from literature on this subject but I can contribute from my own observations. The large accipitrine passage down the Jordan Valley and across the Gulf of Suez comprises eagles, kites, neophron, a few buzzard but none of the true falcons, the small kestrel group, nor harriers nor the goshawk-sparrowhawk group. I have observed it twice in spring and three times in autumn and have never seen a single member of the passage break off for a meal, though at Elath on the Gulf of Aqaba the municipal dump provided a well-found restaurant for the travellers, all of whom are carrion-eaters.

The peregrine appears to feed as he travels; though when travelling in company with other hawks, as I once witnessed in Egypt in spring, they travel without food. I think it quite possible that most hawks which travel in company, with the exception of the kestrels (*tinnunculus*, *naumanni* and *vespertinus*), travel without food; but the three last-named kestrels, travelling in loose flock, feed their way along, often delaying a considerable time if a good feeding-ground is met with. Another exception is the merlin (*Falco columbarius*) which I have seen travelling in flock and resting on passage in Egypt; they fed readily and greedily when resting on passage. Harriers, if in flock, do not delay their journey for food but if travelling independently they feed as they travel. My only records of migration of the sparrowhawks (*nisus* and *badius*) are that they travel in flock, rest for a short time, feed vigorously and pass on. Buzzards travelling in loose flock will not delay for food but if travelling independently will do so. I have no records of the honey-buzzard's sustenance on migration.

Biological precedence

I do not like this term but cannot think of a better one. It is intended to express precedence at food, the animal which gives way to another thereby acknowledging precedence. Take the first instance. A lammergeier comes down to a carcase, is driven away by a raven, who in turn has to take a back seat when the eagle arrives, and the eagle makes way for a griffon vulture who in turn is driven off by a dog; and they all sit around waiting for the dog to finish. Most of the following cases are from my personal observation.

27

Accipitrines
Village dog—Griffon Vulture—Golden Eagle—Raven—Lammergeier (Crete)
Fox—Golden Eagle—Raven (Scotland)
Cinereous Vulture—Griffon and Rüppell's Vultures (Arabia)
Egyptian Vulture—Black Kite (Arabia and Africa)
Bateleur—Four Ground Hornbills (Kenya)
Raven—Lammergeier—Black Kite (Afghanistan)
Two Ravens—Golden Eagle (Scotland)
One Raven—Buzzard (Scotland)
Merlin—Raven (Scotland)
Merlin—Four Hooded Crows (Scotland)
Tawny Eagle—Bateleur—Raven (Aden)
Six Pied Crows—Bateleur (Kenya)
Village dog—Himalayan Griffon—Lammergeier (Sikkim)
Vulture (*Bengalensis*)—King Vulture (Manipur)
White-necked Raven—Bateleur (Kenya)
Griffon Vulture—Egyptian Vulture—Marabou (Sudan)
Two Golden Eagles—twenty-eight Condors (Petersen)

Various
Glaucous—Greater Black-backed—Herring Gull
Glaucous—Iceland Gull
Hooded Crow—Herring Gull
Lion—Three Hyenas—Jackal—Vultures
Eight wild dogs—lion—leopard
Lion—Two wild dogs—Hyena
Ibex—Chamois—Roe-deer (Hediger)
One Tibetan Dog—Three wolves over a sheep they killed
The Marabou takes precedence once the carcase is opened by Vultures
Nearly all large mammals, including the rhinoceros, have the greatest respect for a warthog

Locust Birds

I remember asking an eminent South African ornithologist what was meant by Locust Birds and he replied the white stork and the pratincole. But in fact it includes almost every bird which eats Orthoptera, from crows, rollers and bee-eaters to many hawks, storks and the plover tribe, shrikes and many insectivorous birds. The wattled starling (*Creatophora carunculata*) has also been cited as the locust bird of South Africa. Stark (*B. S. Africa*, I, p. 4) says that these starlings are so dependent on locusts that they are compelled to contact swarms for the greater part of the year; their technique is to surround and intercept part of the swarm.

I have been fortunate in seeing three vast locust swarms in Africa, one of hoppers in Cape Province, one of flying locusts in the Transvaal and another of flying locusts in Kenya.

The hoppers were at Middelburg (Cape) and so numerous that trains were held up owing to squashed bodies greasing the lines so that engine wheels would not bite the rails, and my battalion of over 800 men with large numbers of local people were put on to dig trenches in front of the invaders, who were heading east; when the trenches were full, paraffin was poured on the solid mass in the trenches and a match applied. But even so, it made little impression on the swarm which continued to spread east. I well remember my first view of this swarm—just a black mass of slowly moving fat-bodied hoppers with not a bird in sight in the early morning. The first bird to arrive was a secretary bird; he was soon gorged to repletion; then a small party of kestrel and red-footed falcon, followed by a pack of white stork; by 10 a.m. I could see birds coming from all directions, no doubt attracted by first-comers, until the concourse was immense—rollers, bee-eaters, pratincoles, grey shrikes, a few Abdim's stork, kites, harriers, buzzard and one or two eagles. As many of these birds were seldom seen at Middelburg, they must have collected from a huge area and been guided as vultures are, by watching the 'off-to-food' flight of others, as though a dinner bell was calling children to their meal.

My second introduction to locusts was at Standerton in the Transvaal. Quite suddenly the whole area was shrouded in clouds of these insects flying and settling, constantly on the move and constantly stopping to eat up anything green. The invasion lasted from about 2 p.m. until dusk and the next day no locust was to be seen. The only birds feeding on them were a party of hobbies, a few lesser kestrel and a large party, several hundred, of white stork. Many of the storks were so gorged that they were still sitting about like old gentlemen after a City dinner, complacent, replete and somnolent. The small hawks caught all they wanted in the air and consumed their prey in the air.

My third introduction to a locust swarm was on the Athi Plain in Kenya; they arrived from the south and the swarm moved north, devouring as they went. So dense were they that I could approach hartebeeste and wildebeeste to within a few yards on open grassland. All manner of birds were with this host, several secretary birds and Kori bustard taking insects on the ground, a small party of ground hornbill, hundreds of rollers, mostly European, several Abdim's stork, a few white stork and several marabou, whilst above were countless numbers of kestrel, both European and lesser, and a few red-footed falcon, catching and feeding on the wing.

A minor locust swarm was encountered in extreme north-west Cape Province near Springbok in May; hundreds of kestrel and crows (*albus*) were feeding on them, the crows dismembering them on the ground, the kestrels taking them in the air; as we were watching them a few Cape rooks appeared. Both larks and coursers in small numbers were gorging themselves.

In the Egyptian Sudan, a minor swarm of winged locusts had attracted several marabou, a few buzzard eagles (*Butastur*) and hooded vultures (*Necrosyrtes*), both white and Abdim's stork, many kites, a single swallow-tailed kite (*Chelictinia*) and a few rollers and bee-eaters. The last four species were dismembering and eating the insects on the wing.

Smith and Popov (*Entomologist*, 1953, p. 3) give a graphic account of birds attacking swarms of desert locust in Eritrea on 8 November 1951. White and black storks, black kites, lanner falcons and four species of eagle were involved. 'Although many eagles were on the ground, the majority were in flight up to great heights in very large numbers covering the entire dome of the sky in tier upon tier; they were not counted but some thousands were visible.' There were about a thousand white storks and another thousand marabou. It was not thought that this vast congregation of birds had any appreciable effect on the swarm of locusts.

Locusts are large insects. I doubt if a kestrel could manage more than twenty in a day and a stork would be replete after sixty or seventy, a marabou might manage a hundred twice a day. Even so, the vast congregation of birds I saw at Middelburg feeding on hoppers could not have consumed more than a million and such a small quantity could not have made an appreciable effect on the swarm, for the birds and our trenches combined must have killed hundreds of millions of insects, and still they swarmed.

For further information on locusts and locust-birds, see:

McMartin, A., *The Natural Enemies of Locusts*, Dept. Agr., Pretoria, 1935.

Smith, K. D., and Popov, 'On birds attacking desert locust swarms in Eritrea,' *Entomologist*, LVIII, VI, 1935.

Vesey Fitzgerald, 'Birds as predators of the red locust,' *Ostrich*, 1955, p. 128.

The bird-snake relationship

The relationship between snakes and birds is not a happy one, in fact the snake is in general regarded with fear and disgust by all animal life except those which prey on him. Every living creature is against him and he is against every living creature. They are more commonly preyed on by birds than is generally supposed. Many hawks such as the secretary bird, bateleur, and others enjoy them. The American road-runner is an habitual snake killer. Herons, storks, ibises and domestic chickens will kill and eat them and the pheasant has been known to kill them. There are cases on record where even the missel-thrush and the blackbird will kill them. I once saw a white domestic duck kill and dismember a slow worm.

Near Taveta in Kenya I was watching a pair of plantain-eaters (*Turacus hartlaubi*) feeding on berries, flying up and snatching them much as a flycatcher jumps up after a fly on the wing. A barbet (*Lybius melanopterus*) entered the scene and also commenced to feed on berries. As he did so, a large green snake, almost certainly *Dendraspis*, which I had not noticed, seized him. The plantain-eaters abandoned their meal in great excitement, throwing out their scarlet wings with which they repeatedly struck at the body of the snake who was powerless to retaliate with a dead barbet in his mouth (see plate 5, facing p. 37). The snake commenced to retreat into thick foliage but before he disappeared from view his green body received a sound pecking from the plantain-eaters.

FALCONRY TERMS

Terms used in falconry for the sexes of hawks

	Female	*Male*
Peregrine	Falcon	Tiercel
Gyr-falcon	Jerfalcon	Jerkin
Merlin	Merlin	Jack
Hobby	Hobby	Robin
Sparrowhawk	Sparrowhawk	Musket
Lanner	Lanner	Lanneret
Saker	Saker	Sakret

PREDATORS — AMATEUR

★

Submersion by Reptiles

★

Submersion by Mammals

33

AMATEURS

THE CROW FAMILY
Corvidae

THOUGH not strictly predators, the crow family do on occasions make murderous attacks on other birds and, of course, they are inveterate egg-stealers, though not to the extent which our game-keepers and game preservers would have us believe. In our London garden we have a pair of carrion crows and a pair of jays breeding in an area of seven acres; many wood-pigeon and blackbirds bring off their young annually, the only sufferers being a pair of missel-thrushes, whose early exposed nest gets robbed about once in seven years by the crows. Again, in the west of Ireland, where the magpie is extremely common, hedgerow birds are even more abundant than they are in Britain; it is true that game birds are very scarce, but that is due to the inability of the Irishman to resist killing game regardless of season, ownership or the law.

Magpies and jays, two of the most attractive and beautiful birds of the countryside, are ruthlessly persecuted and shot by gamekeepers and sportsmen with the mentalities of keepers; the harm they do to game birds is negligible; the pleasure they give to the public is immense. Moreover, I know of estates where both jays and magpies abound alongside an abundance of not only game but other small birds. To destroy these birds in order to give pleasure to men who enjoy killing other birds is morally wrong and cannot be justified.

The raven throughout its range is normally a scavenger but will sometimes attack living animals, sickly or half-abandoned lambs, etc. That ravens will kill lambs is certain, especially during or immediately after birth; they will also come down to ewes giving birth in order to feast on the afterbirth. Igalffy (*Larus*, 1948, p. 138) records a raven 'sitting on the back of a sheep and knocking it hard with its bill'; and Kumlien (*U.S. Nat. Mus. Bull.*, xv, 1879) records ravens killing young hares, seals and reindeer. Rubey (*Bird Lore*, xxv, 1933, pp. 143-5) records being set upon in Wyoming by a flock of ravens. 'About thirty of them rushed at us in long vertical dives, croaking, snarling and almost barking out their harsh notes. So real did their attacks appear that we threw rocks in an effort to drive them off . . . but soon the ravens tired of their sport.' Rubey also records flocks of these ravens mobbing golden eagles for fun and also flocks of snow finches, 'the ravens diving swiftly and noisily through the thickest of the compact flock, scattering it, then charging again each time it reformed'.

There is constant war between ravens and peregrines, and there are many records of the former being driven to ground. When attacked in the air by peregrines the raven turns on its back so that the heavy bill can be brought into action. Powyss (*Somerset Essays*) records a herring gull attacking three ravens, the latter turning on the gull and killing it.

In Sinai I have seen the desert raven (*ruficollis*) single out a dotterel from a flock, tire it out by superior speed, drive it to earth, and kill it with a blow on the head with its heavy bill. In all cases of attack by the crow family the bill is used on the head of the victim before it is seized by the feet.

Tinbergen (*Brit. B.*, 1953, p. 377) records the raven in Greenland as preying on ptarmigan, even striking them on the wing, and of a carrion crow striking a lapwing in the air in Northumberland. Howard (*Field*, 6th March 1958) records carrion crows striking and killing partridges in flight. Arnold (*Brit. B.*, 1955, p. 91) records a carrion crow catching a bat in flight, and there are several records of carrion crows catching live fish. They are known to attack waders on the foreshore, often picking up a wounded or sick bird, and they have been known to kill wood-pigeon, leverets and rabbits. In St James's Park I saw a pair pick up and carry off two baby ducks caught on the lawn, and Fitter in *London's Birds* records a carrion crow chasing a heron in London and forcing it to disgorge. Salim Ali (*Journ. Bombay N.H. Soc.*, 1952, p. 666) records a house crow (*C. splendens*) catching and deliberately drowning a rat in Burma; deliberate death by drowning shows sense and is known to be practised by both cormorants and pelicans when dealing with warm-blooded victims. Acharya (*Journ. Bombay N.H. Soc.*, 1951, p. 169) records crows skimming and diving for fish over water with apparent success in India.

Many murderous attacks by the smaller crows are recorded. The pied crow of Africa is known to kill and eat fruit bats (Benson, *Ostrich*, 1946, p. 314). Pitman records (*epist.*) the same crow trying to get at a nest with young of a bulbul. The nest was on a very thin branch, too thin for the crow, so the

PLATE 5

Plantain Eater and Green Mamba

bird alighted heavily on the thin branch a little way from the nest; this acted as a springboard and the young bulbuls were shot out of the nest, falling to the ground, where the crow devoured them. Kirkpatrick (*Journ. Mammalogy*, 1950, pp. 322-7) records predations of the crow (*C. brachyrhynchos*) on the cottontail rabbit (*Sylvilagus*). The cottontail is unable to defend its young, which are a common item of prey in the spring. Once a nest is discovered, typical crow wariness is modified or abandoned. Discovery of the nest is probably due to the sound of squealing young, which are killed, dismembered and, if small enough, swallowed on the spot. K. Eates (*epist.*) records the house crow (*C. splendens*) regularly killing sparrows and carrying them off in the beak, two birds sometimes co-operating, one driving birds from a bush while the other catches them on the wing. In Mandalay I have seen this same crow raiding sparrows' nests and pulling the young to pieces, and on another occasion one of these crows pursued and caught a wounded snipe which it would have eaten if I had not interfered. Even the rook is not innocent of violence. Mrs Cowdy (*epist.*) records seven or eight mobbing and damaging a magpie to such an extent that it had to be killed.

Magpies will occasionally catch and kill small Passerines in flight. In North Sweden I saw a magpie swoop down on a flock of redpolls (*Carduelis linaria*) and seizing one in its feet, make off with it. In west Ireland I saw a magpie with semi-flexed wings swoop down on a flock of siskin (*Carduelis spinus*), and though he made a determined effort to grab one with his feet, the victim escaped. Dr Buchholz of Bonn has kindly sent me an account of a magpie attacking yellow buntings (*Emberiza citrinella*) in Germany and seizing one in its feet. Other similar records come from Canada.

Magpies are more pirates than predators, though on occasions they will kill young birds and small rodents. C. R. Verner (*epist.*) records a magpie catching a half-grown rat and flying off with it. Sage (*Brit. B.*, 1956, p. 353) records a magpie robbing a kestrel (*Falco tinnunculus*) of its prey, alighting on the kestrel's back and pecking its head until the kestrel dropped its prey. Mitchell (*Field*, 20th March 1958) records three magpies attacking and killing a grass snake, all injuries being behind the head and none on the body. Mountfort (*Portrait of a Wilderness*) records a magpie in southern Spain killing and eating a two-foot snake.

Dixon (*Condor*, 1933, p. 161) records three magpies coming on a golden eagle eating a squirrel. They mobbed it until the eagle had to relinquish its prey and defend itself, when one of the magpies sneaked in and carried off the squirrel, which was 'later shared—*without fighting*—with the other two magpies.' Dixon adds 'Was this robbery planned?'

SHRIKES, DRONGOS AND TITS

The largest of all shrikes, the grey-backed fiscal (*excubitorius*), is the only shrike which does not appear to prey on small birds, and it is the only shrike which habitually goes about in small parties, the others being almost always solitary or in pairs. Pitman (*Ann. Reports Uganda Game Dept.*, 1937, p. 27) records one attacking a small snake.

All the true shrikes are bullies, aggressive and bloodthirsty, catching small birds, especially helpless young, and beating out the brain, which is eaten, the body being usually discarded. When not chasing small birds they prey on insects or small lizards. Birds as large as a wheatear are chased in and out of bushes, the victim often taking refuge down a hole. The grey shrike (*excubitor*) has been known to catch a swallow, and Baron Geyr von Schweppenburg (*epist.*) records one following a flock of linnets and securing one with its feet. The red-backed shrike (*collurio*) is said to have caught a sand-martin on the wing, and there are many records of small birds, mice and lizards being killed. Even the small masked shrike (*nubicus*) has been seen chasing a warbler (*Prinia*) in Palestine.

Rana quotes from Hill (*Condor*, 1945, p. 149) the case of a shrike (*L. ludovicianus*) seizing a small rodent from the clutches of the American sparrow-hawk (*Falco sparverius*).

Norbeck and Melin (*Var. Fagelv.*, 1955, p. 240) record the red-backed shrike 'having a good time feeding on warblers.'

The so-called larder of shrikes appears to be an unnecessary habit. I have had many larders of shrikes under observation in Britain, Africa and in India and I have not yet seen a shrike return to the larder for a feed off an impaled victim. But I have seen shrikes examine their larder and pick off beetles and maggots. In many cases a larder once formed is apparently forgotten. The red-backed shrike has been seen impaling insects on blades of grass and later taking them to its young. Both thorn and barbed wire are used for impaling victims.

Thielcke (*Zeitschrift für Tierpsychologie*, 1956, pp. 272-7) finds that the great grey shrike sitting on a high perch will recognise a mouse at eighty yards. Most prey is dropped on from the perch, the bill striking the neck of a mouse at the same moment as the feet touch the ground; the head is struck several times before the mouse is killed; if a mouse is seen for only a moment the shrike will alight near by and on the mouse's reappearance will pounce on it from a few feet. The mouse is seized by the bill and transferred to the claws only after taking wing; light prey is carried in the bill only. Mice are impaled on thorns or wedged between forked branches; when eating vertebrates, all shrikes commence at the head, the entrails being discarded; the meal may take up to an hour and a half.

Bigalke (*epist.*) records the drongo (*Dicrurus adsimilis*) catching and eating sunbirds in South West Africa.

The true tits have an insatiable taste for meat. Cases have been recorded of them killing other birds as large as themselves and eating the brain (Stewart, *Auk*, 1955, p. 83, and Diesselhorst, *Auk*, 1956, p. 558). Caris (*Brit. B.* 1958: 355) records a great tit killing and carrying a goldcrest in its feet in Cumberland. I have noticed that in my London garden both blue and great tits will prefer meat to either coconut or milk.

DIVING BY PASSERINES

The activities of many amateur predators and pirates involve diving, and though this is mainly confined to non-Passerine birds there are a few cases of incipient diving by Passerines which are cited here. In dealing with the diving of non-Passerines (p. 43 et seqq.) I have made full use of records published by Atkinson, Bahr, Coward, Dewar, Hollom, Millais, Taylor and Salmon. My own records were taken by stop-watch.

Incipient diving occurs in that lovely Asiatic bird *Enicurus*, a denizen of rushing water and spray, whose tail is frayed by splash and plumage spangled like drops of rain. I have seen them walking in and under water in search of insect life and even in fast-running water they appear to be able to move not only against the current but across and with it, grasping small pebbles and rough rocks to counter gravity. I have never seen complete submersion for more than four seconds.

D

The dipper (*Cinclus*) is a slightly better exponent; the ingenious theory that a dipper uses the force of the current on his sloping back to maintain depth is untenable. He uses his feet to grasp pebbles and stones, and also his wings—the latter predominantly. A wounded dipper in Afghanistan was driven downstream to where I stood; it was a fast-running stream about two feet deep. The bird passed between my legs, both wings in use. In Yorkshire and in the Pyrenees I have seen dippers walking on the bottom without using their wings. When a dipper surfaces he bobs up like a cork; it is therefore difficult to understand how he balances buoyancy under water when he moves without using his wings, unless he grasps rough rock, pebbles or water vegetation.

In Yorkshire I have watched complete submersion for between 6 and 11 seconds. On the Tibetan plateau, where the dipper remains for the winter despite a below-zero temperature, I have seen them diving through a hole in the ice and remaining below ice for 22 seconds; and that in a fast-running torrent where both foothold and swimming must be precarious.

CUCKOOS TO COLIES

Among the cuckoos, the coucal (*Centropus*), in both Asia and Africa, is a killer of small birds, searching for nests and devouring eggs and young. C. Benson (*Ibis*, 1945, p. 92) records *Centropus superciliosus* eating a barbet (*Pogoniulus*) in Kenya.

Rollers (*Coracias*) include small birds and reptiles in their diet and are particularly fond of frogs. In Estonia there is an authentic case of a whole brood of baby wryneck (*Iynx*) being eaten by a roller and in Kenya a roller has been known to catch and eat a sandgrouse chick near Marsabit.

The larger kingfishers (*Alcedinidae*) regularly kill small reptiles and frogs. W. W. Phillips (*epist.*) records the Smyrna kingfisher in Ceylon catching a white-eye (*Zosterops*), beating it to death and swallowing it whole.

Even the mouse bird (*Colius striatus*) is a predator. Pitman (*Ann. Report Uganda Game Dept.*, 1937, p. 26) records one carrying off from the nest a newly hatched chick of a sunbird. And near Nanyuki in Kenya I have seen a party of mouse birds mobbing a small chameleon until it dropped to the ground, when the mob of mouse birds followed it down, killed it and pulled it to pieces.

PLATE 6

Ground Hornbills and Black Mamba

GROUND HORNBILL

Bucorvus cafer

The food of the ground hornbill consists mainly of insects, small rodents and young birds, lizards and snakes. Tortoises are much relished, all the flesh, including the head and limbs, being neatly picked away, leaving a clean and undamaged carapace. But occasionally the ground hornbill, usually in small parties, will tackle large and dangerous snakes.

Ayres (*Ibis*, 1861, p. 132) gives the following account: 'On discovering a snake, three or four of the birds will advance sideways towards it, with their wings stretched to irritate the snake till he seizes them by the wing feathers, when they immediately close round and give him violent pecks with their long sharp bills, quickly withdrawing again when the snake leaves his hold. This they repeat till the snake is dead. If the reptile advances on them, they place both wings in front of them, completely covering their heads and most vulnerable parts.'

I witnessed a somewhat similar scene on the Serengeti Plains between Voi and Taveta in Kenya. On some recently burned grassland was a party of ground hornbills strutting about like turkey. Some of them soon became excited and commenced to dance around. I stalked them and got within 100 yards. There were seven birds in all, walking and dancing round in a circle, trailing their wings like amorous farmyard cocks and constantly poking their heads at something in their midst which I recognised as a large black mamba, erect for about a third of its length and swaying backwards and forwards, constantly lunging at the birds, each lunge being received on the pinions of the trailing wings. The birds would often run in and try and peck the snake, the snake would strike, down came the wing to receive the poisonous fangs and the birds would try to get in another peck before the head and neck recovered to an erect position. The hornbills appreciated the fact that the snake was dangerous and were content and intent on wearing him out by pecking. The contest lasted some twenty minutes. The end came when it was clear from the strikes of the snake that he was nearing exhaustion. His activity became less and less and he did not recover so quickly from his lunges. Then suddenly after a particularly weak lunge, all the birds, as if by signal, rushed and pecked and stamped on that snake until he must have been pulp. There was a whirl of dust and feathers and wriggling snake, all lashed up

41

together and then all was still, the birds commencing quite quietly to pull their victim to pieces. I then drove the birds off their kill. The snake was nine feet long. I left him, and the birds soon returned to their well-earned meal.

Near Nyeri in Kenya I have seen a ground hornbill pick up a small snake and, rising about twenty feet into the air, drop it on to hard ground before pulling it to pieces and eating it.

All hornbills are mischievous; they enjoy teasing other birds and mammals, especially monkey, and appear to have a sense of humour usually accompanied by a sadistic tendency. Any occupied nest found is promptly pulled to pieces, eggs destroyed and fledglings either thrown to the ground or swallowed. Pitman (*epist.*) records the African hornbills (*Bycanistes subcylindricus* and *Tockus alboterminatus*) raiding weaver colonies and sunbird nests in Entebbe and devouring the young. *Bycanistes* would sometimes take a whole sunbird's nest in its bill and squeeze it.

There are several cases of hornbills in both Asia and Africa catching and swallowing small bats, and in Kenya I have seen them chasing the large tree-top beetle in the Kabwuren Forest. Any small mammal or reptile caught in the open is first of all teased, then thrown up into the air, caught and swallowed.

MARABOU
Leptoptilus crumeniferus

The marabou stork in Africa is mainly a carrion and garbage feeder but will also eat helpless young birds. It is believed that in 1956, when the greater flamingo bred on Lake Elmenteita in Kenya, many marabou descended and ate not only the dead chicks but also many living ones.

Marabou will often soar at great heights with vultures and probably depend more on watching vultures than in finding food for themselves. They prefer attending slaughter-houses, municipal dumps and Somali camps, often remaining in the vicinity for days on end, roosting in neighbouring trees. The largest congregation I have seen was at Muhoroni during the Nandi expedition of 1906 when thousands of cattle and sheep were concentrated and badly cared for. I counted over 500 birds.

A marabou cannot tackle a carcase until it has been opened up by vultures or other carrion-eating animals; but once the carcase is opened up, in steps the marabou, and he will not tolerate a vulture within pecking distance when he is feeding. I have seen a small bunch of marabou feeding on a dead cow at a Somali camp with many vultures sitting around waiting their turn.

On the Nile I have seen marabou walking solemnly along in shallow water feeding on small molluscs and fish. Pitman (*Bull. B.O.C.*, 1957, p. 110) records marabou preying on crocodile eggs and hatching crocodiles.

I have on several occasions seen marabou parading or resting in or near crocodile-infested waters; in both Somaliland and Kenya I have asked Africans whether the marabou is immune to attack by crocodiles and in every case I have been assured that it is.

HERONS AND BITTERNS
Ardeidae

Though primarily fish-eaters, this group will prey on small rodents, frogs and other birds. The bittern (*Botaurus*) has been known to kill and devour a full-grown water rail and has been seen to 'spike' a kingfisher. The common heron, though usually preying on coarse fish, will readily prey on rodents and small birds if they come his way. In Sinai I have seen the common heron in absolute desert, searching for rodents, lizards, and even beetles.

Both the common heron and egrets have been seen diving for fish from flight.

SWANS, GEESE AND DUCK
Anatidae

I have never seen a swan dive, nor can I imagine an occasion when it is necessary. But geese can dive to escape predators, though it is a clumsy proceeding. When wounded a goose can dive and remain submerged with only its beak showing. Surface-feeding duck all dive well, using their wings and feet under water, and to escape predators they will dive from flight. I have seen both widgeon and teal dive from flight when chased by a peregrine; I have seen scoter plunge into the sea from several feet when chased by a glaucous gull, and off Iceland I saw a whole flock of long-tailed duck dive from flight when chased by a great skua.

Though swans do not dive, the mute swan is an aggressive bird, resenting whoopers and Bewicks invading their territory even in winter. Mayfield (*Auk*, 1952, p. 461) records a captive whooper killing mallard ducklings and suspected of killing young Canada geese. Wilson (*Journ. Bombay N.H. Soc.*, LII, p. 666) records a swan on the Liffey near Dublin making its way upstream when a cormorant surfaced a few feet away with an eel in its beak. The swan attacked, the cormorant dropped the eel and dived. The cormorant then surfaced close to the swan, when the former seized the latter's neck and held the head under water. A drowned swan floated downstream and the cormorant continued fishing.

The mallard of Greenland is a sea duck and has developed regular diving habits, entailing skeletal differences approaching those of the true diving duck. I watched a party of seven diving in Greenland in water 20 feet deep; both wings and feet are used when diving. Submersion lasts from 32 to 56 seconds, but when scared they can remain below the surface for 88 seconds and then only the bill is above water.

Even such slob-gobbling ducks as the sheld-duck (*Tadorna*) and the ruddy sheld-duck (*Casarca*) can dive when wounded and will surface with but the bill showing. How buoyancy is compensated is a mystery.

The diving duck vary greatly in their duration of submersion. Red-crested pochard on Lake Antioch were observed to dive in shallow water for 36, 41 and 53 seconds and when scared for 64 seconds. The pochards and tufted duck are shallow divers, seldom above 30 feet and usually much less, submersion lasting more than 40 seconds, the longest being that of the common pochard in South Uist which reached 47 seconds in about 10 feet of water. The scaup feeds in much deeper water and submersion has been recorded up to 60 seconds (Cordeaux), Dewar giving 49 seconds in 21 feet of water.

The goldeneye (*Bucephala*) is a shallow-water duck averaging 25 seconds submersion though 55 seconds have been recorded (Alford). Dewar gives 36 seconds in 13 feet of water. Barrow's goldeneye was observed diving in Lake Myvatn when in eclipse and with half-grown primaries in but 8 feet of water, submersion lasting 18, 24 and 26 seconds.

The long-tailed duck (*Clangula*) is a shallow-water feeder, sometimes so shallow that complete submersion is impossible, the feet kicking up spouts of water and the wings not being used. Usual submersion is from 30 to 60 seconds, the longest record being 90 seconds.

In Greenland I saw 8 ducklings diving to avoid a long-tailed skua, submersion varying from 17 to 22 seconds.

The harlequin duck (*Histrionicus*) was observed in Iceland only on fast-running streams, diving with use of legs and slightly flexed wings; dives are sometimes made from a projecting rock several feet above water; when feeding under water they were seen to face upstream only, with both wings and legs going full out to face fast-running water. Submersion was observed for 18 and 26 seconds only, but Alford gives maximum as 28 seconds.

I have only seen Steller's eider once, at Petsamo in north Finland (now Russia) in mid-winter. They were feeding in 24 feet of water and submersion on three occasions was for 37, 34 and 42 seconds.

The common eider (*Somateria mollissima*) feeds in fairly shallow water, sometimes close inshore and rarely in water over 20 feet deep; they submerge for from 32 to 54 seconds (8 counts). A scared drake in the Sound of Harris submerged for 1 minute 42 seconds in his first dive, 1 minute 36 seconds in his second dive and only 42 seconds his third dive. On several occasions I have seen them in Scotland surface with crabs 3-4 inches across and dismember them on the surface, but small shells are swallowed below the surface.

The king eider (*Somateria spectabilis*), though a smaller bird than the common eider, feeds in deeper water. At Petsamo they were feeding in 7 fathoms and in Greenland males in eclipse were feeding in 10 fathoms, and as they are solely bottom feeders that is some dive. Eight dives in 7 fathoms ranged from 62 to 78 seconds and in 10 fathoms from 54 to 83 seconds. In both cases the stomachs contained nothing but mollusca, prawns and small crabs. All swallowing is done below surface.

The common, velvet and surf scoters (*Oedemia nigra*, *fusca* and *perspicillata*) appear to have much the same feeding habits, the diet being mainly mollusca, especially small mussels; also small prawns, shrimps, and occasionally shells. I have never seen either species diving in more than about 20 feet of water. Submersion is for from 20 to 35 seconds but Dewar records up to 50. A scared velvet scoter submerged for 64 seconds in the Dornoch Firth.

I have seen all three species of scoter diving. When submerging the wing is sometimes flexed, sometimes closed, but they always use the feet; they dive straight down and sometimes at a slight angle to the vertical. Both feet are used in unison. When surfacing, the rise is usually vertical and rarely in a spiral ascent. A figure of the vertical ascent is given in the *Auk*, 1957, p. 392.

45

I can add nothing new about the goosander (*Mergus merganser*), which I have never observed feeding. In Ladak on the River Indus a scared bird submerged for 104 seconds but her ducklings, only a few days old, could only manage 10-15 seconds. The adult used her wings when diving. It is usually a river bird, diving in shallow water.

The merganser (*Mergus serrator*) is an estuary and shallow-water diver, submerging for from 28 to 47 seconds, and both wings and feet are used in diving. A scared bird in less than 6 feet of water remained submerged for 118 seconds and in the second dive for 82 seconds.

I have seen the smew (*Mergus albellus*) diving in fresh water in Hampshire where water varied from 6 to 12 feet, and 3 dives lasted 24, 25 and 27 seconds. In Baluchistan 4 dives in 20 feet of water lasted 12, 17, 21 and 34 seconds and in one case the partly flexed wings were used.

In 1916 at Naivasha in Kenya I observed a pair of maccoa duck (*Erismatura*) feeding on a patch of open water in papyrus swamp. It appeared that the wings are not used under water; 10 dives extended between 54 and 101 seconds.

Most diving birds employ one method of propulsion on the surface and another when diving. When surface-swimming the webbed feet are used forwards and backwards, the webs extended in the backward stroke and contracted in the forward stroke; the other method is the sculling or oblique method, legs being held to the side and moved forward and backwards like man with an oar. This method is rarely used on the surface, but I have seen diving duck in St James's Park use it while travelling on the surface.

In under-water diving cormorants, grebes, divers and all diving duck use the sculling method of propulsion; so do coot.

Brooks (*Auk*, 1945, pp. 517-23) claims that the alula or bastard wing is always fully extended when diving but I cannot confirm this.

GREBES AND DIVERS
Podiceps and *Gavia*

Opinion differs as to whether divers use their wings under water or not. They probably do and don't. On the only two occasions when I have been able to witness an under-water dive, the great northern (*immer*) did not use his wings and the red-throated (*stellatus*) did. The period of dive is between 57

46

and 110 seconds, but when scared a great northern diver can manage 134 seconds under water. The great northern has been caught in nets at 200 feet below the surface (Schorger, *Wilson Bull.*, p. 151). The main food of all divers is free-swimming fish; they are not bottom feeders.

Coward records a dive of three minutes for a wounded bird but this may be an error, for a wounded diver can expose only his bill for one or two seconds and this is seldom observed. For a combined attack by great skua and diver on eider, see p. 58.

I have only had two opportunities of watching grebes under water and in neither case were the wings used; they are shallow-water feeders, seldom in more than 12 feet, though I have seen the great crested fishing in 40 feet of water in the Baltic. Dives vary from 35 to 65 seconds in the larger grebes and between 20 and 54 in the smaller species. Though fish is the main diet, all aquatic insect life is taken, also small crustacea and mollusca. In nearly every grebe I have shot there have been a few feathers: the reason for this has not yet been explained. Small feathers are also fed to the young.

Many years ago at Tring I watched a parent great crested grebe with three babies, the latter boarding their parent by the rump. I clapped my hands and waved a paper at them; the parent submerged, leaving the babies afloat; one dived for about a second, then they all swam about excitedly in circles looking for their parent. I threw a stone near them, the splash making them all dive for about 3 seconds. Having answered my enquiry I left them alone.

The young of the little grebe when less than a week old can submerge for 6–10 seconds and when ten days old for 15–20 seconds.

THE PELICANS
Pelecanus

Pelicans have two techniques when fishing, the one an organised drive commencing in crescent formation and ending in a complete circle, and the other diving from flight like a gannet.

I saw a successful fishing in the Crimea by the Dalmatian pelican (*crispus*). There were over a hundred birds forming line, driving towards shore in shallow water, the two ends of the line advancing in perfect order and not very fast. A crescent was eventually formed, every bird keeping his correct

47

station, and then, as water barely 18 in. deep was reached, the two horns of the crescent increased speed, closed in, and formed a complete circle, the birds almost touching. Within the circle the water boiled with small fish, heads were rapidly plunged in simultaneously and pouches filled with fish, the circle closing in all the time and feet paddling hard to prevent fish escaping below body-line. It is then all over; birds quietly disperse and digest or, if the meal is inadequate, another line is formed and the process repeated. Gulls, terns and cormorants know all about it and crowd in to pick up stray fish, but they keep well out of the reach of the pelican's strong and ruthless bill. A cormorant which came too near the line was seized, ducked and flew off in alarm, having learned not to interfere and poach.

In Balaclava harbour I saw a single bird dive from about fifty feet, closing his wings at the last moment—a terrific splash, complete submersion and a ten-inch fish. This was held in the pouch for at least a minute before being swallowed.

The white pelican (*onochrotalus*) has much the same habits as the Dalmatian.

In captivity they have developed a most reprehensible habit. In the Zoological Gardens at Giza near Cairo, where many wild duck take refuge by day, this pelican can be seen sidling up to a teal, suddenly seizing it, holding it under water until drowned and then swallowing it. They have also been seen to snap at sparrows in St James's Park in London.

On Lake Chrissie in the eastern Transvaal I have seen the pink-backed pelican (*rufescens*) in water so shallow that they could not swim, but neverthe-less fishing in crescent formation and paddling with their legs though standing up, and finally not dipping the head to catch the fish, but scooping them out.

I have only seen the brown pelican (*occidentalis*) in California, where it seemed that diving for fish was more usual than co-operative fishing. It is a beautiful sight seeing these heavy birds diving from a great height and hitting the water with a huge splash, but the technique is slightly different from that of the gannet.

Murphy (*Oceanic B.*) gives a good description of the dive. 'The twisting descent is doubtless responsible for the fact that the bird turns some sort of somersault under water and comes up heading in another direction from that of its diagonal dive. Emergence, in fact, finds a pelican facing the wind and ready for flight while the plunge is usually, if not always, with the breeze astern. As soon as pelicans surface they turn down the bill to drain the pouch . . . after which they toss up and open the bill so as to release their victim, only to receive it in the throat and swallow it with a gulp. It is at such times that the laughing gull and noddies attempt to steal the prey of the pelican, sometimes standing on the latter's head.'

FRIGATE OR MAN-O'-WAR BIRDS
Fregata

I have seen three species engaged in piratical war—*aquila*, *minor* and *ariel*. Their technique is much the same as that of the skuas but they are faster on the wing and more relentless. It is said they have a larger wing area for body weight than any other bird of about their own size. The gannet (*Sula*) family are their favourite prey, though they will also attack gulls, pelicans, cormorants, and tropic birds. They are also said to eat young turtles. Murphy (*Oceanic B.*, II, p. 937) thinks they do their own fishing in rough weather, resorting to piratical work in calm weather. They are particularly fond of flying fish which they catch as they fly, and will often pick fish off the surface but without ever diving.

When attacking the gannet family they stoop and harry the bird relentlessly until the fish is disgorged when it is caught in the air. Any hesitation to disgorge on the gannet's part is followed by a contact attack, the powerful bill being used to strike the gannet on the back. Off the north coast of Madagascar I have seen the same gannet robbed on three consecutive occasions, the pirate waiting on quite close while the gannet fished; in fact, the gannet appears to realise he will get no peace and no fish until the frigate bird's appetite is satisfied.

GANNETS
Sula

Though the usual technique of gannets is to dive for fish from the air, other methods have been recorded. In January 1951 when passing Perim Island at the south end of the Red Sea we had several gannets, both *leucogaster* and *melanops*, cruising alongside the ship at about 14 miles an hour and flying at wave height. They were attempting to catch flying fish on the wing as the ship disturbed them. I witnessed dozens of attempts but only one catch; the bird at once settled on the water and swallowed; but their purpose was obvious.

When diving for fish, submersion is for between 5 and 12 seconds and the depth of a dive has been recorded as 180 feet, a record rejected by Winterbottom (*Ostrich*, 1955, p. 44). Alexander (*Birds of the Ocean*, 1928) gives the depth of dive as 90 feet and this is confirmed by Courtenay-Latimer (*Ostrich*, 1955, p. 44). But in the first place, would a gannet see a fish at 90 feet even in clear tropical waters? Secondly, if a depth of 90 feet were attained by a diving gannet, the under-water period would exceed 20 seconds. After the plunge gannets will often surface with wings fully extended.

Barlee (*Shell Aviation News*, Feb. 1956) believes that the shock wave caused by the impact of a gannet striking the water when diving may stun the fish just below the surface up to a distance of perhaps 6 feet.

The gannet has been observed dibbling for sand-eels in 2 inches of water and also making shallow dives for fish in only 2-3 feet of water (*Brit. B.*, 1952, p. 420). They are also attracted to basking sharks.

In the Sound of Harris I came across a great northern diver struggling with a fish too large to swallow; two gannets were sitting on the water within a foot of him and making feeble efforts to pirate the fish; eventually one of them struck the diver in the neck; his mouth being fully occupied, he could not retaliate so he submerged; the gannets sat on the surface looking rather stupid; the diver surfaced about fifty yards distant and the gannets immediately flew to him and again tried to secure the fish from the diver's mouth; the diver submerged again, I scared the gannets away and left the diver in peace to struggle with his one-pound fish.

J. E. Flynn (*Brit. B.*, 1957, p. 537) records gannets pirating large gulls in Ireland in August; the gannets 'would plunge in a shallow-angled frontal dive at the gull, entering the water about two yards away and snatching the fish from the gull's bill on breaking the surface . . . the gannets also frequently fluttered along the water, snatching fish from other gulls as they passed.' Most of the pirating was done against immature gulls owing to their inability to move quickly.

I have seen the gannet (*melanops*) close inshore at Port Sudan diving almost vertically with success in but 3 feet of water from a considerable height: how this is achieved without collision with the bottom is not apparent.

CORMORANTS, SHAGS AND DARTERS
Phalacrocorax and *Anhinga*

The cormorant (*carbo*) will fish in fresh or salt water, the shag (*aristotelis*) only in salt; and despite the fact that the cormorant is the larger bird, he fishes in shallower water than does the shag. Cormorants will wander far inland to lakes and up rivers, but not the shag. The cormorant only remains on the water when fishing; when replete they resort to roosting and drying places on sand spits, cliffs or on buildings. These are regularly used all round the year; the largest I have seen being a sand spit off the coast of South West Africa where many thousands of birds were resting and drying themselves. Another large resting and drying place used to be on the roof of the Sultan's Palace in Constantinople; the combined fire brigades of that city failed to dislodge them. Cormorants and darters are unique among diving birds in that their plumage becomes drenched when diving despite the fact that the wing is scarcely ever opened under water.

Cormorants will eat 17 per cent of their body weight daily; a heavy cormorant weighs about 4,000 grammes or nearly nine pounds; that means about a pound and a half of fish a day. In Shetland, where they frequent the mouths of streams up which sea trout run, I watched three birds fishing; one very old bird caught a half-pound sea trout and a small eel on two successive dives; the fish was swallowed on the water but there was trouble with the eel and the cormorant had to land on the bank with the eel's body entwined round its neck and covering it with slime; the struggle to get free lasted about twenty minutes, the feet being freely used to try and unravel the coils of the eel; when it was finally swallowed the cormorant's neck was plastered with slime, and I then witnessed the pectinated middle claw come into use with frequent visits to the water to clean. That cormorant was then replete, perhaps too replete, for he remained on the bank until roosting time.

The other two cormorants on that stream made dozens of dives without success and finally flew off to other water.

Off Cornwall I have frequently watched shags and cormorants fishing. I have counted as many as fifty consecutive unsuccessful dives by each species; on the other hand another bird may be successful after a single dive. Free-swimming fish are the usual prey though small flat fish are often taken in estuaries.

51

Neither shags nor cormorants use their wings under water but propel themselves with simultaneous strokes of both feet. When swimming on the surface they use their feet alternately; their usual dive is from 30 to 45 seconds, rarely up to 78 seconds, and when frightened they can manage 104 seconds under water.

The following are records of dive duration of other cormorants. The small cormorant (*niger*) submerged in 7 feet of water in Manipur for from 21 to 38 seconds (11 counts) and when scared for 49 and 83 seconds.

Another small cormorant (*africanus*) has been timed on the Victoria Nyanza and on Lake Naivasha. On the former lake 8 dives in water of unknown depth varied from 18 to 34 seconds and when scared 37 and 62 seconds.

The pygmy cormorant (*pygmaeus*) has been timed on Lake Antioch and in Afghanistan in shallow water barely 8 feet deep; 8 dives varied from 19 to 42 seconds.

The Socotra cormorant (*nigrogularis*) was timed at Bahrein in water varying from 8 to 32 feet and submerged when feeding for from 24 to 51 seconds and when scared up to 74 seconds.

In Walfisch Bay in from 18 to 24 feet of water, the cormorant *neglectus* dived for from 32 to 48 seconds and when scared up to 64 seconds.

The Californian cormorant (*penicillata*) at San Diego in water from 18 to 37 feet averaged 42 seconds submersion in 18 dives and when scared could dive up to 74 seconds.

I have watched the darter (*anhinga*) fishing in many parts of Africa, on Lake Antioch, in India and Iraq. They do not use their wings when under water and fish in much shallower water than either shag or cormorant and often among reeds. I have never observed submergence for more than 52 seconds and I have seen as many as 50 unsuccessful dives in succession. Capt. Pitman records (*Ann. Records Uganda Game Dept.*, 1937, p. 25) that in Uganda during the course of 17 minutes he saw a darter make 28 dives, of which 25 were successful.

Nestling cormorants and shags have not yet developed the pectination of the claw of the middle toe, nor do they need it until they fish for themselves. Another curious fact about nestling cormorants is the invariable occurrence of small pebbles in the stomach, though these are rare in adults. It has been suggested that these are taken in whilst the young play with each other, catching pebbles thrown by other chicks, but that is most unlikely.

TROPIC BIRDS
Phaethon

I have seen these glorious birds (both *rubricauda* and *lepturus*) fishing in hundreds off Mauritius, sometimes as many as several hundred at one place. They dive from about 40-100 feet, often preceded by a hover, then a slanting dive, not so steep or vertical as that of gannets and boobies, and usually enter the water slantwise, often with a spiral twist. Submersion seldom lasts for more than a second or two.

PETRELS
Procellariiformes

The fulmar has been observed diving from a surface position in Greenland, complete submersion lasting for a few seconds only.

The diving petrels (*Pelecanoides*) dive for from 3 to 20 seconds (Murphy, *Oceanic B.*).

PLOVERS, RAILS

Even some of the plover tribe will become predators. W. W. A. Phillips (*epist.*) records the yellow-wattled lapwing (*Lobipluvia*) in Ceylon seizing a chick of the finch-lark (*Eremopterix*), battering it to death and swallowing it.

Among the rail family, Mrs Cowdy (*epist.*) records that while a pair of little grebe on Blenheim Lake were putting finishing touches to their nest a coot arrived and tore the nest to pieces, both grebes swimming round close by and uttering a shrill call; having completed the destruction the coot swam away. Was the coot searching for eggs or young, or just objecting to grebes nesting in its territory?

Of all birds the coot (*Fulica*) excels in spite and aggressiveness; they are always snappish and bad-tempered; being mainly colonial, they have a highly developed territorial sense. In Baluchistan and again on Lake Naivasha in Kenya I have seen them deliberately destroy nests of grebes and duck (*Erismatura*) who presumed to nest near them. Their up-splashing defence against predators is well known and they are skilled scratchers with their

53

sharp claws. A favourite defence is to lie on their back and use their claws, which in efficiency surpasses the technique of a gin-sodden virago.

K. Eates (*epist.*, Oct. 1957) had a tame gallinule (*Porphyrio poliocephalus*) in India which frequently caught and ate fledgling sparrows and on one occasion caught and ate a young plover (*Sarcogrammus indicus*).

On the lake in St James's Park I have seen coot systematically drowning newly hatched duck; they are indeed the finest exponents of the world's worst vices—jealousy and spite.

THE GULLS
Laridae

The predatory habits of the larger gulls are well known. Their unashamed persistence and ruthlessness in robbery and piracy is only equalled by the habits of the skuas. No birds are more ready to take advantage of the weak or wounded than the larger gulls, which pick out living eyes and rend living flesh.

In Orkney I have seen the greater black-backed deliberately waylaying puffins returning with food to their young, striking them down over land, smacking them on the head and devouring them.

At Handa in Sutherland I lay down within a few feet of a ledge on which eight guillemots were brooding eggs. We will call them G.1 to G.8. Two herring gulls were also on the ledge. There was the usual quarrelling among the guillemots, pecking and making faces at each other. The gulls were there awaiting their opportunity to steal eggs. We will call them HG.1 and HG.2. HG.1 sidled towards G.1 who at once snaked its head and resented the approach; HG.1 persisted in its approach, compelling G.1 to uncover her egg and raise herself. HG.2 at once stole the egg, breached it and commenced to feed whilst its owner looked around stupidly, did not appear to notice the thief standing over the broken egg, and generally made itself a nuisance to the other sitting birds. HG.1 now joined HG.2 and they both fed off the egg. Having finished their repast they both walked slowly in among the sitting guillemots; an uproar ensued, all birds raising themselves, HG.2 stole G.2's egg, broke it at once and commenced to feed, receiving a hard peck from G.2 and G.3. HG.2 opened his wings which caused G.2 and G.3 to retire. But HG.1 had now got G.3's egg. Meanwhile G.1, still wandering around, took possession of an uncovered egg and commenced to brood. The other seven were much disturbed, for there were now three eggs gone and three eggless guillemots wandering around stupidly. A greater black-backed gull now arrived on the scene, in alighting buffeting two guillemots with his wings and causing much more snaking and scolding and rising up. The new gull seized his opportunity in the confusion and stole an egg, commencing to feed at once. All the guillemots were now off their eggs, an opportunity at once taken by HG.1 and HG.2 who took yet another egg before they had finished G.2's and G.3's eggs. But G.1 would not move from her adopted egg. G.2, who was 'bridled,' hurried off to brood G.5's egg. So now we had five eggless guillemots and two sitting on eggs which were not their own. By the evening there were but two eggs left and six disconsolate guillemots on the ledge. A week later there were six guillemots on that ledge with eggs. Whether these guillemots were new arrivals or second-brooders is guesswork. But I do not understand how such piracy can go on and has been going on for centuries without some diminution of the guillemot population, which is single-egged and said to be single-brooded.

The greater black-backed gull (*L. marinus*), the glaucous-winged gull (*L. glaucescens*) and the glaucous gull (*L. hyperboreus*) have been known to snatch food from both sea ducks and divers; and in the Cromarty Firth I have seen the common gull (*L. canus*) harrying a grebe (*Podiceps*) until it gave up its food.

On another occasion in Caithness, when peering down near Dunnett Head into one of those mysterious little voes or miniature fjords, I saw a parent shag trying to regurgitate food to its single young on a rocky ledge. Right against them stood a herring gull, bent on interference. His presence was not in the least resented. As fast as food was regurgitated the gull interposed his bill right into the parent shag's gullet and committed an act of robbery. The parent shag flew off, returning in about half an hour, and a similar procedure ensued, the young shag getting but a portion of its parent's regurgitation. The remarkable part was the complete absence of resentment on the part of the shag, who apparently thought it quite natural that a robber gull should insist on a portion of the offspring's food.

Cobb (*Auk*, 1957, p. 498) records a gull (*marinus*) in Massachusetts recognising a wounded duck, chasing it and making it dive until exhausted when the gull seized it 'by the neck, pulled it to the surface and shook it vigorously for about four minutes.' Feeding commenced from the breast.

The larger gulls nesting on a grouse moor probably do more damage than all the ravens, crows, foxes and stoats; nor are new-born lambs free from their attentions. It is curious that a ewe with a new-born lamb will react at once to ravens, eagles or foxes, but I have never noticed any reaction towards gulls; I have seen a ewe paying no attention to a gull pecking the eyes of her offspring.

In east Sutherland and again in Shetland I had several divers' nests under observation. In every case there were near-by colonies of lesser black-backed gulls. Though the divers' eggs were often uncovered for long periods, never once were the eggs touched though gulls would often pass close over the nests. But greenshanks' and plovers' nests were ruthlessly robbed though the eggs were less conspicuous. Is a diver's egg unpalatable?

In the large fulmar colonies in Greenland there is a constant patrol of glaucous and Iceland gulls ready to snatch any unprotected chick or egg; and it is remarkable that I have never seen any co-operative movement among fulmar directed against these marauders. Terns and smaller gull colonies will concentrate on a marauder.

Bent (*Bull. U.S. Nat. Mus.*, 1946, No. 191) records that the Californian gull (*Larus californicus*) destroyed 18 per cent of 3,000 waterfowl eggs and were responsible for a 40 per cent decrease on the average duck brood; they were responsible for the destruction of about 30 per cent of the waterfowl eggs and young produced.

The black-headed gull (*ridibundus*) is not above mobbing, not only for protection but for food. They have been seen (Cowdy, *epist.*) mobbing coot on Tring Reservoirs for food, and will concentrate for mob action against ravens, crows and skuas when breeding whilst paying no attention at all to peregrines or buzzard.

There are several records of the black-headed gull pirating various species of diving duck. B. L. Sage (*Brit. B.*, 1955, p. 177) records: 'The general procedure adopted by the gulls to obtain food in this manner is to make a sudden attack on the duck immediately it surfaces in the hope that it will be induced to drop whatever it has brought up, which is then picked up by the gull. Actual snatching of food from the victim appears to be less common. It may therefore be worth placing on record that on 22 November 1954, at

56

PLATE 7

Arctic Skua

a gravel pit near Radlett, Hertfordshire, I watched two gulls of this species attending a small flock of tufted duck (*Aythya fuligula*) in the manner described above. On one occasion, however, one of the gulls hovered above the spot where a duck had submerged, and immediately this bird surfaced near by the gull alighted on its back, and maintaining its balance with open wings, snatched something from the duck's bill.' I have seen similar attempts by the same gull to take food from diving tufted duck in St James's Park, but the duck always managed to dive again and avoid acts of piracy.

SKUAS
Stercorarius

The great skua is primarily a pirate but also a predator. He is quite capable of finding food for himself but prefers the greater exertion of pirating gannets, gulls and terns.

Dr Gudmundsson (*epist.* 1956) tells me that the great skua will kill adult mallard and eider, their method being to tire them out by forcing them to dive continuously and then cracking their skull with their bill when the victim is thoroughly exhausted. But that the skua will also fish for himself at times.

I have seen this skua attack duck at sea, the technique being to land on the victim's back and hammer the skull. I have observed this with sheld-duck, eider, scoter and long-tailed duck. Almost always the duck manages to dive and then the skua hangs about, and as soon as the victim surfaces the attack is resumed until the duck is exhausted. This technique often succeeds where a single bird or a pair are involved; but duck know the technique and will, if they can, join another flock of duck, when numbers cause confusion and the skua makes off.

Campbell and Denzey (*Brit. B.*, 1954, p. 403) record this skua killing a heron in Shetland. The skua 'swooped on a heron from above, apparently striking with its feet at its victim's back, but also holding with its beak, for both fell together to the water; there, the skua, on the heron's back, continued its attack by pecking repeatedly at the head of its prey, at the same time using a paddling action with its feet, as if to force the heron under water. The heron finally succumbed'—probably by drowning.

Another case of a skua using its feet to attack a gannet is recorded by

Stirling (*Scott. Nat.*, 1951, pp. 133-5), and Moran (*Field*, 9 May 1957) records this skua killing a lesser black-backed gull in Shetland, tearing out its entrails and trampling on it.

At Hoy in Orkney in 1938 there were twenty-four pair of great skua breeding, their main food being kittiwake and puffin; we found the remains of many dozen of these birds and we estimated that about fifty victims must be secured every day. The skuas would lie in wait for the puffins returning to their burrows, quickly assault them, knock them on the head and at once commence to eat the breast. Often the puffin, laden with fish, would slip into his hole before the skua could catch him. But the skua knew his job and would wait just above the hole and knock the wretched puffin out as he emerged. We noticed at Hoy that ravens give the skua a wide berth but peregrines and harriers usually ignore them, though the latter is attacked if it approaches the nest. We never saw a skua molest a fulmar at Hoy, though the latter was abundant.

In Shetland this skua is abundant. In August I witnessed a remarkable combined operation against an eider and her brood by this skua and a great northern diver. The eider had three very small ducklings. The skua would swoop down, compelling them to dive, whilst the diver would submerge and, catching them under water, would surface and swallow them. In the end, the skua secured one duckling while the diver secured another. The third duckling disappeared and must have been secured by either the skua or the diver. The skua sat on the water to eat his duckling.

A. Hazelwood (personal communication) records that in autumn the great skua when attacking eider utters a loud call which attracts kittiwake who later partake of the feast when the skua has finished.

The local crofters begged us to shoot all the skuas as they had lost seven lambs from attacks in one spring. Also in Shetland we noticed that small colonies of terns were powerless to resist an attack by skuas and in every small colony not a single chick got off, but in the larger colonies combined action by the terns would beat off an attack.

Again in Shetland, we saw as many as twenty-five of these skuas cruising about at Noss Head where some 3,000 gannets were feeding their chicks; the skuas would watch for a gannet returning with food, though how a gannet with food could be distinguished from a gannet without food is difficult to explain. A gannet would be selected and several skuas would accelerate and

PLATE 8

Gannet and Skua

pursue. The gannet would turn away, dive to sea level and make for the open sea with the skuas in pursuit. The leading skua would fly up from behind and, catching the gannet by the tip of the wing with its bill, would tilt him into the sea in an undignified crash, screaming hard. The skua would retain hold of the gannet until he disgorged. On two occasions the skua pecked the gannet's body until he disgorged. By this time several skuas, and perhaps a great black-backed gull, would be on the scene, and a scramble would ensue for the gannet's fish. I counted eleven attacks on gannets by skuas in fifteen minutes, all of which were successful from the skuas' point of view.

At the same place I saw five of these skuas attack and kill an immature gannet which had fallen from its nest into the sea. Attacked at first by a single skua, the gannet, almost full grown, put up a fight with its bill and by terrifying the skua with a wide-open mouth. But other skuas, seeing the attack in progress, joined in, and delivering blow after blow with their powerful bills, soon swamped the gannet who was promptly torn to pieces and devoured.

In the North Atlantic I have often seen this skua following ships; very occasionally they would forage for refuse by themselves, picking it off the sea; but more often they would wait until a gull descended on a morsel and then attack it, following it until it disgorged. W. W. A. Phillips (*epist.* 27 Oct. 1957) records two great skuas attacking a great shearwater (*Procellaria gravis*), driving it to the surface and making it disgorge.

A fulmar petrel's reaction to aggression by skuas is counter-aggression.

Of the smaller skuas the Arctic (*Stercorarius parasiticus*) is the one with which I am most familiar when at work. In addition to depredations on land among young birds he is an inveterate pirate and bully when at sea. Terns are his main source of food and the method of attack is peculiar. I have never seen an Arctic skua actually striking a tern nor do other violence than buffeting, colliding and striking with the wing. When the great skua attacks, definite acts of violence are committed; when the fishing eagle pirates the osprey bodily contact is made and blows are exchanged; but the Arctic skua is content with smothering the flight of his victim by violent aerobatics at very close quarters, often ending in collision. I have never once seen feathers fly or any sign of injury done. Victory is mainly psychological. Surrender by the victim occurs when food is given up, sometimes almost as soon as the attack develops but often after considerable and repeated acts of buffeting, the skua slowly driving his victim lower and lower.

I have seen an Arctic skua stoop at black guillemots when feeding, but evasive action by diving is easy and effective. The skua will then sit sheepishly on the water where the victim dived and await its reappearance. Off he goes after it but another dive defeats him and he will then usually abandon the chase.

In Greenland I witnessed three Arctic skuas pursuing a small compact flock of sanderling one of whom was unable to maintain his place in the flock for some reason. It was soon overtaken, hit on the head and torn to pieces by the three skuas.

Young cuckoos pass through Shetland in some numbers in autumn and are commonly chased, usually over land, easily caught and hit on the head by the bill of both great and Arctic skuas; on one occasion I saw an Arctic skua buffet the cuckoo with its wings until it fell to the ground when the skua landed and struck it on the head. On one island off Shetland we found the remains of seven young cuckoo thus intercepted when on passage.

In Greenland, where the Arctic and long-tailed skuas (*longicaudus*) are common and usually in fair numbers near large terneries, we noticed that they never actually entered the terneries but hung around outside, intercepting terns carrying food for their young or going out to sea and pirating fishing terns. Though food was abundant they preferred piracy to fending for themselves. An attempt by a long-tailed skua to kill some ducklings of the long-tailed duck was thwarted, partly by the attitude of the parent and partly by the little victims' prolonged diving.

AUKS, RAZORBILLS, PUFFINS AND GUILLEMOTS
Alle, *Alca*, *Fratercula* and *Uria*

The whole of this group use their wings under water and their feet as lateral sculls.

The little auk (*Alle*) will take small fish, crabs and mollusca. They will feed in water where bottom feeding is impossible owing to depth, but prefer water under 30 feet in depth. In 15 feet of water in Greenland I counted 27 dives varying from 22 to 41 seconds, but when scared they can keep submerged for 71 seconds. When feeding they almost always surface some distance from where the dive is commenced.

The razorbill (*Alca torda*) has been observed swimming on its back under water (King, *Brit. B.*, 1952, p. 430). Food is about 50 per cent small fish, probably mostly sand-eels, but they often fish in water over 100 fathoms deep where bottom fishing is impossible. Fish are swallowed both on the surface and under water. When carrying food to young as many as twelve sand-eels have been recorded in the mouth 'all arranged in a regular row at right angles to the bill' (Frohawk, *Brit. B.*, v, p. 90). The period of submersion varies from 24 to 61 seconds, but if scared they can remain submerged for 74 seconds.

The puffin (*Fratercula*) is usually a fisher in shallow waters during the breeding season, but in winter he will fish in water of over a hundred fathoms where he could not possibly reach the bottom. When they are not feeding young, the prey is swallowed under water. Submersion varies from 24 to 31 seconds, rarely to 42, though when scared they can remain submerged up to 58 seconds.

The ingenuity displayed by the puffin in being able to catch fish when he may already have several dangling in his mouth, had often puzzled me. I suspected that captured fish were held in position by the tongue, which would enable the bird to open his bill and catch further fish. But my problem was to catch a puffin alive with fish in his mouth. After several unsuccessful attempts at Handa (Sutherland) I finally did so, by lying flat among tufts of thrift and with my hand just above a burrow down which I had seen parent puffins enter with fish. I caught the bird by the head, clamping my fingers over the powerful bill, and was then able to examine his secret at leisure. The fish were all dangling tail out from the mouth, two on one side and three on the other, and were held in position by the tongue clamping against the upper mandible. I then let the bird go after marking his upper mandible with indelible pencil. He was back at the nest in less than forty minutes with more fish—the same quantity and arranged in precisely the same manner as when I caught him up.

I obtained a puffin in the Isles of Scilly as he was bringing food to his young. Eight young transparent sand-eels were dangling from his mouth, heads inside and four on each side. Each fish was about two inches long. Fortunately I was able to handle the bird with his bill still closed. On examining the manner in which the fish were held I found that the heads were all clamped by the tongue against the roof of the upper mandible. On the same day I watched a puffin feeding its young. The fish were presented to the chick who took the one nearest the tip of the mandible first, then the second then

61

the third until the whole of one side was exhausted; a similar act of acceptance was then performed on the other side of the mandible, commencing at the tip and working towards the gape. The upper surface of a puffin's tongue is deeply grooved for this purpose.

The black guillemot (*Uria grylle*) uses his wings and feet under water and usually fishes in shallower water than most auks. They almost always surface at point of diving, which lasts from 34 to 56 seconds, rarely 50 seconds and once 78 seconds. They will sometimes dive in only 18 inches of water close inshore. The main diet of adults is crustacea and mollusca and, in immature birds, small fish and occasionally sea-weed. This is reflected in the colour pigment of the fat and soft parts, that of the adults being vermilion and of the immatures pale orange, pink or even pinkish white.

The common guillemot (*Uria aalge*) swims with wings and feet under water; dives in Shetland included one of 71 seconds, eight between 50 and 62 seconds, eleven between 40 and 50 seconds, twenty-five between 20 and 40 seconds and five of under 20 seconds. Birds surfaced far from the point of submersion. A scared bird dived for 92 seconds. The stomachs of seven birds in Shetland in August contained about 65 per cent small fish and about 30 per cent crustacea and small shells; a very little seaweed.

The habits of Brunnich's guillemot (*Uria lomvia*) are identical with those of the common guillemot; five Greenland birds examined in August had 15 per cent of small fish and the remainder prawns and shrimps. Submersion when fishing varies from 54 to 71 seconds but a scared bird can dive for 98 seconds. Food is swallowed under water.

PENGUINS
Spheniscidae

The period of submersion of *Pygoscelis papua* is from 6 to 7 minutes and of *Eudyptes chrysolophus* from $3\frac{1}{2}$ to 5 minutes (Scholander, *Hvalradets Skrifter*, 1940).

I have watched the jackass penguin (*Spheniscus demersus*) fishing off Cape Town and in South West Africa. The usual period of submersion is from 62 to 89 seconds but on one occasion lasted for 1 minute 24 seconds.

Roberts (*Brit. Grahamsland Exped. 1934–1937*, 1, 3) gives the maximum period of submersion for *Pygoscelis papua* as 6 minutes and for *Eudyptes chrysolophus* as 2 minutes, after which the bird is exhausted.

Penguins probably feed not below 15 feet but have been taken in nets at 80 fathoms, though it is not known at what depth the bird entered the net.

The under-water speed of *Pygoscelis adeliae* is between 8·1 and 8·5 miles per hour, and that of *Aptenodytes patagonica* 6·9–7·8 miles per hour, timed in the London Zoo over distances varying between 50 and 85 feet by stop-watch.

★   ★   ★

SUBMERSION BY REPTILES

Crocodiles. I watched a crocodile about 10 feet long in a pool on the Nzoia River in 1906. There was no weed or cover of any sort where he might have poked his nose up. His surfacing for air took place at intervals of 21, 35 and 47 minutes. Schmidt, in *Crocodile Hunting in America*, 1952, p. 16, says: 'In 15 or 20 minutes he is compelled to come to the surface for air.' But Pope in *Reptile World*, 1956, p. 9, says: 'Experiments have shown that at least the American alligator can remain under water as long as five hours before drowning.'

Sea snakes. In Karachi in 1914 I found a black-and-yellow-banded sea snake in a pool of salt water. I frightened him by throwing stones at him and then watched for surfacing. He came to the surface after 3 hours and 18 minutes.

But Curran and Kauffeld in *Snakes and their Ways*, 1937, p. 180, say of sea snakes: 'It is not known just how long they can remain submerged, but reliable investigations indicate a period of at least eight hours.'

I am indebted to Dr H. W. Parker for drawing my attention to the above reference.

★   ★   ★

SUBMERSION BY MAMMALS

A bottle-nosed whale has been known to submerge for two consecutive hours even with a harpoon embedded in him; their usual period of submersion is from 30 to 45 minutes.

63

Sperm whales usually submerge for between 30 and 45 minutes, with a maximum of one hour.

The fin and blue whales submerge for between 5 and 15 minutes (Scholander, *Hvalradets Skrifter*, XXII, 1940, and Roberts, *Brit. Grahamland Exped. Sci. Reports*, I (3), pp. 246-7).

PREDATORS — PROFESSIONAL

True Vultures	Cinereous Vulture
Egyptian Vulture	Palm-nut Vulture
Lammergeier or Lammervanger Harriers	Marsh Harrier
Pallid Harrier	Hen-Harrier
Montagu's, Black, and Pied Harriers	Harrier-Hawk
Bateleur	Serpent Eagle
Black-breasted Harrier-Eagle	Brown Harrier-Eagle
Osprey	Caracara
Pygmy Falcon	The Gyr-Falcons
Lanner	Saker
Jugger	Peregrine
Taita Falcon	Merlin
Sooty Falcon	Eleonora's Falcon
Hobby	Lesser Kestrel
Kestrel	Red-legged Falcon

PLATE 9

Mackinder's Owl

PROFESSIONALS

EAGLE OWL
Bubo bubo

USUALLY nocturnal in habit, though commencing to hunt immediately after sundown. In Ladak one's first evidence of their
presence was the deep hoot as they emerged from a rock shelter
when one could just see to shoot. After about a quarter of an hour's hooting
there would be silence and hunting would commence. Six pellets examined
contained nothing but the remains of rodents.

At Mottisfont in the winter of 1891–2 a single bird appeared at Lockerley,
took up residence in a well-stocked pheasant covert and was of course
shot as vermin by a keeper, the usual fate of a rare bird who interferes with
sport.

Lord Lilford describes in his paper on the Birds of the Ionian Islands how
near Butrinto this owl came flying past him in a hurried manner and took
refuge in a bush just as a peregrine falcon stooped at him. The owl was
driven out and the falcon made several stoops, the owl dodging among the
bushes and finally taking refuge in an olive grove.

In the Syrian Desert I have seen this owl sitting in bushes barely 4 feet
high during the day and feeding on nothing but rodents. Of eight pellets
examined all were mammals.

The only kill I have witnessed was in Estonia, when I was watching a
small covey of hazelhen (*Bonasia*) under pine. Suddenly an object like a sack
dropped from a tree on to one of the birds below and I did not recognise it
as an eagle owl until he extended his wings to screen his capture. After waiting
barely a minute he commenced to feed. This was an exceptional case, as it
occurred in the middle of the afternoon.

Both jays and crows are taken when roosting. Six pellets obtained near
Abisco in Swedish Lapland contained only the bones of crows and the
Siberian jay (*Cractes*).

67

In the Ahaggar Mountains of the Central Sahara, a large number of pellets were obtained from a cave where a pair had taken up residence : these were examined for me by the late Percy Lowe and contained nothing but the remains of small mammals and some bones of a little owl (*Athene*).

Kroneisl (*Larus*, 1948, p. 139) records eight coleoptera, three mice and one wren (*Troglodytes*) from the stomach of an eagle owl in April 1948.

On a large estate near Hanover in 1897, roe-deer were regarded as a regular food of the eagle owl. Mostly young were taken and these were often successfully defended by the parent. Throat wounds indicated strangulation. On one occasion the roe hind struck the owl with her sharp little feet, knocked it down and continued to buffet it until it was so badly knocked about that it lay helpless when it was recovered by a keeper; I now have the skin in my collection.

Dr Meise (*Deutscher Falkenorder*, 1936, p. 2) records this owl killing a roe-deer weighing almost 30 lb.; and Meise and Zimmermann (*Orn. Monatsb.*, 1936, pp. 55-8) give more cases where this owl has killed roe-deer, partly by strangulation and partly by piercing the vertebrae immediately behind the skull. But the killing of roe-deer by this owl must be exceptional, probably resulting from a single owl having successfully killed a young and feeble animal.

Grimes (S. A. Grimes, *Florida Naturalist*, 1936, pp. 77-8) records this owl attacking a snake 46 inches long; the owl was lying on its side with outstretched wings trying to get its talons into the snake, which was coiled twice round its abdomen. The beak was not used. The owl was exhausted and flew off with the snake dangling. Mr Grimes then shot the bird.

There are many cases of this owl attacking man and dogs. Death is achieved by crush and by biting the back of the head.

Norman Wilkinson (*Bird Lore*, 1913, p. 369) records an attack by this owl on a skunk. 'His feet were thrust forward, firmly grasping a full-grown skunk. One foot had hold of the skunk's neck and the other clutched it by the middle of the back; the animal seemed to be nearly dead but had strength enough to leap occasionally into the air in its endeavours to shake off its captor. During the struggle the owl's eyes would fairly blaze and he would snap his beak with a noise like the clapping of the hands.'

They have also been known to tackle a porcupine, a dead bird being found with 56 quills in it.

PLATE 10

Snowy Owl

SNOWY OWL
Nyctea nyctea

The snowy owl hunts by daylight and by the poor light of an Arctic winter. Its hunting flight is low, the prey being taken by surprise and usually eaten at the place of killing; they will also ascend to considerable height and drop on prey with flexed wings. They will pursue duck, ptarmigan and pigeon in follow-chase, seizing their victim in the air. They often quarter the ground about fifty feet up, hovering when a victim is sighted and then dropping with closed wings or gliding down at a steep angle.

Recorded prey is various—from hares and lemmings to small voles, and from black-game and guillemots to snow buntings. Birds as large as ravens and buzzard have been recorded. Fish are recorded in this diet, more in America than in Europe. In Arctic Canada this owl is practically confined to lowland areas where lemming abound (Watson, *Ibis*, 1957, pp. 421, 459).

When attacking the large Arctic hare they have been seen to grasp the hare with one foot and use the other as a brake in the snow or herbage; they will also use their wings as brakes when being dragged along by their victims.

Brewster (*Bull. Mus. Comp. Zool.*, 1925, pp. 221-402) records a case of a man surprising this owl in the act of killing a chicken; the owl, instead of trying to escape, faced the man and refused to leave its victim.

I have only once seen this owl—in Greenland. It was sitting or rather lying down on a small rock beside a channel of sea water; it allowed me to approach within 30 yards before it stood up and bobbed its head at me; owing to deep water I could not approach the bird who I thought was wounded, but in fact I believe he was fishing. After admiring this magnificent owl for well over half an hour I threw a stone into the water near him and off he flew over the tundra hotly pursued by skuas.

Audubon (*B. America*, 1840, VOL. I) describes the method this owl employs when fishing. While watching for fish 'they invariably lay flat on a rock with the body placed lengthwise along the border of the hole, the head also laid down, but turned towards the water. One might have supposed the bird sound asleep, as it would remain in the same position until a good opportunity of securing a fish occurred; when a fish appeared the owl would thrust out a foot and with the quickness of lightning seize it.'

There is a case on record of this owl being mobbed and killed by terns in Greenland.

Giaever (*In the Land of the Musk Ox*) records a case in East Greenland of a pair of snowy owls and a pair of Arctic fox breeding near each other. One adult owl was wantonly shot and left to rot. One of the foxes found the carcase and devoured it. The owl's nest contained one fairly large chick, one just hatched and five unhatched eggs. The larger chick devoured the newly hatched chick. Then the remaining adult owl killed a fox and gave it to the chick. Meanwhile neither fox nor owl dared leave its young for fear of attack. The surviving fox eventually attacked the surviving chick of the owl but was in turn attacked by the remaining adult owl, which resulted in the death of both fox and owl. This left one half-grown owl and a litter of baby foxes. The owl ate its parent and when satiated left the carcase to be finished off by the young foxes. The young owl then commenced to feed on the surviving young foxes. Such is the struggle for existence and survival of the fittest.

BROWN OWL
Strix aluco

The brown owl is mainly a nocturnal still-hunter but will occasionally start hunting in the evening light. They spend the day in slightly less concealed positions than the long-eared owl, which exposes them to the risk of mobbing, a most annoying small-bird habit for the sleepy and hungry owl. In Kashmir, so common and persistent is this mobbing that we could always trace this owl by the chatter of mobbing.

They will glide or drop like a stone on a victim, indulging entirely in still-hunting; and at the moment of impact will extend their wings either to cover the victim or strike him.

At Mottisfont we knew several of their still-hunting stances; one evening we placed a dead white rat thirty yards from the stance and attached a cord to it, we remaining hidden in a rick. Just as the owl pounced we jerked the string: he sat on the ground looking astonished and with trailing wings ran after the rat until he was almost within touch of our hide. We pulled the rat into the hide and off went the owl to his stance and at once hooted. We threw the rat out again, when the owl descended at lightning speed, seized it and remained sitting on it for half a minute; we then tugged a little; the owl spread his wings and pecked the rat; we tugged again; the owl now attempted to fly off with the rat but the cord held and he was left with but a fragment of skin; the owl continued to his stance and at once hooted, was joined by his mate who at once pounced on the mutilated rat; we then pulled the rat and owl right up to our hide before she loosed her grasp and flew off having given a final hoot within a few feet of us. This made us doubt if hooting has much to do with courtship; it is probably more closely connected with territory.

I know an estate in the north of England where woodcock breed commonly, the sitting bird falling an easy victim to the brown owl, presumably because of the large shining eye of the sitting bird. A woodcock when alarmed keeps its eyes wide open, unlike the nightjar, which closes its eyes to mere slits when alarmed. I believe the light reflected by the eye to be the usual means by which a night-hunting marauder locates its prey. Few nights are so dark as to be completely lightless; the slightest light or the smallest star will reflect from the eye. Man can only see these reflections by using a strong torch or lamp, but the owl with its deep lens would see them if a single star was shining.

The brown owl is said to beat small birds out of bushes with its wings, but I have never observed this procedure. I have known them play havoc in a starling roost, pouncing down into rhododendron from a tree overlooking them.

Our first evidence that brown owls eat worms was at Mottisfont when a keeper brought in a brown owl which had been raiding young pheasants; as usual, no young pheasants were found in the bird, but several worms were in the throat and stomach. Since then I have found worms in an owl's throat in Scotland. Does the brown owl patter for worms as do waders? At Mottisfont we saw an owl pattering and bouncing about on newly mown lawn by moonlight. He would give four or five patters, then bounce to another spot four or five feet away and repeat the process; but we never saw the owl pick up anything, though on several occasions he would place his head on one side as though listening, as do the thrush tribe. Again in London I have seen a brown owl bouncing about on a newly sown flower bed, with occasional pattering with both feet; but no worm was seen to be taken.

Experiments have shown that a brown owl can see twenty times better than man; even so, it is difficult to believe that they can hunt in a darkness which will not affect a photographic film. At Mottisfont we rigged up a small dark room in which it was safe to expose a photographic film for the whole night.   On three successive nights a brown owl, a white owl and a scops owl were placed in this room with a live mouse.   On every occasion the mouse was taken and the owl was found back on his perch in the morning. Sight can have had little to do with the capture of that mouse or with the ability of the bird to regain its perch.   The mouse may have been captured by 'squeak.'

Southern (*Ibis*, 1954, pp. 384-410) gives an analysis of the pellets of 20 pairs of brown owls near Oxford over a period of eight years.   Small rodents predominate in winter and spring and larger mammals in summer and autumn, whilst birds and shrews are taken at a constant rate throughout the year.

Young hares and rabbits are also taken and fish have been recorded as food.

Dr Altum (*Journ. f. Orn.*, 1863, p. 218) after examining 52 pellets records 10 shrews, 11 moles, 48 various mice, 1 squirrel, 12 small birds and insects.

On two occasions I have been very close to brown owls when hooting—once in Hebron and again in Hampshire.   On both occasions the throat was much distended.

LONG-EARED OWL
Asio otus

A purely nocturnal hunter, spending the day in a thick-foliaged tree, usually near the trunk.   I have never observed this owl hunting and the only record I have of a victim was a redwing in Perthshire; the stomach of the redwing was in the owl's stomach and contained many seeds of the bird-cherry, a case of a predator being a plant-spreader.   In America food is 90 per cent small rodents.

AFRICAN MARSH OWL
Asio capensis

This owl hunts by daylight, preferably in the late evening.   I have seen them hunting near Nairobi and observed two kills, a full-grown Hottentot teal and a zorilla; the latter though killed was not eaten, presumably owing to its smell.   Hunting is by flying low over the ground, pouncing and grasp.

In Morocco I have seen them hunting in the middle of the afternoon but never saw a kill though several pounces were observed, in one case the owl systematically searching a clump of long grass from the ground. I suspect this owl hunts by sound as much as by sight.

SHORT-EARED OWL
Asio accipitrinus

Largely an afternoon hunter; in South Uist I have seen them hunting as early as 2 p.m. Though their main diet is voles, they will also take snipe and redshank. The latter was caught in mid-air, the owl's wing striking it, whether deliberately or not I do not know. In North Uist their pellets contained bits of snipe and one bird was infested with snipe feather lice (*Mallophaga*). Both grouse and green plover have been recorded as killed in Orkney.

I had unique opportunities of watching this owl in North Uist in 1947. There were eight pair within a mile of the house. About two hours before sundown they would commence to hunt on fine evenings, sometimes still-hunting from a post but mainly quartering the ground about three feet above ground level. I noticed that when they had located their prey (voles) they would side-slip into the grass with wings outstretched. Twice this was carried out within a few feet of me and on both occasions I noticed the wings were fully stretched, flattening the grass and presumably scooping the vole. I doubt if in either case the owl could have seen the vole through the thick tangle of grass; and so close were the birds to me that I could distinctly see the feathers round the ear protruding and not flat; I believe these owls were hunting by 'squeak.' On another occasion I had an owl hunting quite close to me when it hovered just above the grass, listened and plunged down, capturing a vole which was at once swallowed whole.

I believe that silent flight, such as owls enjoy, is as important in not alarming prey as in enabling the owl to hear well and not be inconvenienced by the sound of its own wings.

I have seen this owl hunting at Lucknow, in Lapland, in the Crimea, and at several places in the British Isles. In Lapland I saw a single bird at noon hovering about 300 feet above a marsh searching for young whimbrel, whose parents mobbed it. The owl suddenly closed its wings and fell like a stone, securing a chick. On another occasion in Lapland a pair of crows commenced to mob an owl who evaded them quickly by gaining height; the crows gave up as they could not compete, leaving the owl a mere speck in the sky.

The largest party of this owl I have seen was on the field of Balaclava in February 1910. I counted over sixty birds sitting about and quartering the ground, which was short grass and infested by voles; it was a pretty sight amid a carpet of yellow crocuses and a golden sunset.

This owl dislikes being mobbed; in the Outer Hebrides I saw some black-headed gulls commence mobbing action against three owls sitting on tussocks; the gulls became bolder and bolder until the three owls rose in their wrath and for some fifteen minutes drove the gulls about and with their superior strength clawed more than one of them.

It often happens that there is a three-day gale in the Outer Hebrides accompanied by pelting rain. Under such conditions it is impossible for either this owl or the hen-harrier to hunt, owing to their light bodies and large expanse of wing. Both these species were grounded, sheltering behind tussocks; after three such days these predators must be consumed with hunger.

Brewster (*Bull. Nuttall Orn. Club*, 1879, p. 13) found a colony of these owls feeding on nestling terns in the U.S.A. At least a hundred had been eaten.

Brewster (*Bull. Mus. Comp. Zool.*, 1925, pp. 211-402) records cases of them mobbing large birds—black ducks and blue herons, probably for amusement. And Jung (*Auk*, 1930, pp. 553-41) records an aerial flight between this owl and a harrier in America, probably in defence of its nest.

HAWK OWL
Surnia ulula

The hawk owl lives in the birch and conifer woods of northern Europe and is diurnal in habit, often sitting in most conspicuous places—telephone poles or on the top of a dead branch. It usually still-hunts though on occasions it will mount fairly high and hover over open country, dropping on prey like a kestrel. It is the only owl I know who consistently resents and attacks small birds who mob it; even the Siberian jay is not immune; grouse are also recorded in its diet. A bold bird, known to have taken a large claw-ful of hair from an egg-collector hoping to rob its nest.

The American race hunts by day and night, usually from a stance on top of a tree or telegraph pole, is both bold and comparatively tame. Food, as large as ruffed grouse and as small as mice.

SCOPS OWL
Otus scops

Hunts by night and sometimes by day; but is usually well concealed in a tree or building by day, commencing to hunt at dusk after a good deal of hooting. In Crete I had exceptional opportunities to observe them as they were abundant not only in the building in which I lived but in many trees and bushes in the vicinity. They would not only pursue moths on the wing but would also sit in convenient places and pounce on moths, especially the oleander hawk moth. I was surprised at the pace a scops could travel when chasing the rapid-flying hawk moth. All captures were seized by the feet and not transferred to the mouth, carried to a tree and eaten, the wings being discarded. Though small bats were common in the neighbourhood, I never saw scops molest them. But in Iraq I saw the race *brucei* constantly chasing bats in Baghdad, and on one occasion a large moth was chased into the Residency dining-room, seized in mid-air and carried out again through the window. Small birds and lizards are rarely taken.

The normal flight is very undulating but when in pursuit the flight is direct and remarkably rapid.

PYGMY OWL
Glaucidium gnoma

Bent (*Bull. U.S. Nat. Mus.*, 1938, p. 417) records one of these small owls pulling a willow woodpecker (*Dryobates pubescens*) from its nesting hole and flying off with it.

LITTLE OWL
Athene noctua

The little owl feeds by both day and night, its main diet being insects, small mammals, lizards, small snakes, and frogs, and it delights in feeding on maggots in putrefying flesh. It has been seen pouncing on sparrows with success and an occasional bird will take chicks from a farmyard. But on the whole it has been proved to be beneficial, though still persecuted by game preservers. I know of two cases where this owl has raided kestrels' nests and taken the young, one case in Hampshire and the other at Tring. Igalffy (*Larus*, 1949, p. 371) records little owls exterminating a colony of breeding swallows.

The little owl is a great seed distributor; on many occasions I have found several varieties of seeds and even grit which can only have come from small Passerines.

BURROWING OWL
Athene cunicularia

Much sentimental nonsense has been written about the beautiful association of this owl with rattlesnakes and prairie-dogs. To quote Elliott Coues (*U.S. Geol. Survey Terr.*, Misc. Publ. No. 3, 1874):

First as to the reptiles, it may be observed that they are like other rattlesnakes, dangerous, venomous creatures; they have no business in the burrows, and are after no good when they do enter. They wriggle into the holes, partly because there is no other place for them to crawl into on the bare, flat plain, and partly in search of owls' eggs, owlets and Prairie-Dog puppies, to eat. The owls are simply attracted to the burrows as the most convenient places for shelter and nidification. . . . Community of interest makes them gregarious to an extent unusual among rapacious birds. . . . That the owls live at ease in the settlements, and on familiar terms with their four-footed neighbours, is an undoubted fact; but that they inhabit the same burrows, or have any intimate domestic relations, is quite another thing. It is no proof that the dogs and birds live together, that they are often seen to scuttle at each others' heels into the same hole when alarmed; for in such a case the two simply seek the nearest shelter, independent of each other. The probability is, that young dogs often furnish a meal for the owls and that, in return, the latter are often robbed of their eggs; while certainly the young of both, and the owls' eggs, are eaten by the snakes.

This owl is also attracted to domestic animals for disturbed insects.

I am much indebted to Mr J. A. King (*epist.*, 22 April 1955) who writes:

The 'Happy family' myth of the burrowing owls, prairie-dogs and rattlesnakes has frequently been exposed. Apparently the reason for the close association is that the prairie-dogs dig numerous burrows which can be utilised by the burrowing owls and rattlesnakes. They probably never occupy the same burrow at one time although the three animals may be found in adjacent burrows.

Rattlesnakes frequently inhabit burrows which are rarely used, at the edge of a prairie-dog town. They often spend the day in the burrows in order to avoid the hot sunshine. Any prairie-dogs venturing near these burrows are probably warned off by the rattle of the snake. Probably the rattlesnakes prey only on the young prairie-dogs since an adult prairie-dog would be too large for them to handle. Besides the refuge of the burrows, the rattlesnakes also come to the town to prey upon other small rodents such as mice and ground squirrels which inhabit the prairie-dog burrows.

I know of only one reference in literature regarding an antagonistic relationship between the prairie-dog and the rattlesnake. This is in the *Journal of Mammalogy*, XIII, pp. 74-5, by O. E. Stephl, who says:

With regard to the burrowing owl, again it appears that they are attracted to prairie-dog burrows simply as a place to nest. When the owls have selected a burrow they are apparently able to drive away the prairie-dogs and keep the burrow to themselves. The prairie-dogs are frightened by the threatening postures of the owls. The owls are very small birds and largely insectivorous. I doubt if they could cause much injury to the prairie-dog. I believe you can understand the reason for the close association of these animals if you primarily consider the importance of nest sites and refuges that are created on the open prairie by the burrowing activities of the prairie-dog. Since the animals are brought together by the presence of refuges, the predator-prey relationships among them are rather negligible, each keeping out of the other's way as much as possible.

WHITE OWL
Tyto alba

The white owl is an habitual daylight hunter, though the custom appears to be more individual than specific. Prefers open country to woodlands. In 1935 I knew a pair in Suffolk which hunted regularly over a marsh at about 3 p.m. in August, whilst at our house in the same district, a pair never emerged until almost dark. In Cornwall I have seen a single bird hunting over the same area and using the same route, day after day in September. At Mottisfont we had a similar experience, the Abbey pair never hunting by day but the Oakley pair hunting in the early afternoon over marshland almost every day in August.

One of the world's most useful predators, the main diet being small mammals. Finley (*Condor*, 1906, pp. 83-8) records a case where 'a half-grown owl was given all the mice it could eat; it swallowed eight in rapid succession. The ninth followed all but the tail which for some time hung out of the bird's mouth . . . and in three hours' time the little glutton was ready for a second meal and swallowed four additional mice.'

I believe this owl hunts almost entirely by flying very low over likely ground in order to be able to listen to squeaks from small rodents. If a squeak is heard they stop abruptly and hover over the spot, only a foot off the grass and sometimes turning the head as though looking for something to connect up with the fatal squeak. See also under the short-eared owl.

Prey is taken by pounce and snatch, the powerful grip causing instant death. At Mottisfont we had evidence of snipe, water vole, blackbird and many smaller rodents being taken, besides a large proportion of moths. Though we had two pairs under observation at Mottisfont and though both pairs shared their quarters with large colonies of bats, we never saw an owl attack a bat nor did we find the remains of bats in pellets. The Abbey pair would take small fish—evidence from pellets only. I have already recorded the case of a kitten being taken and carried off, but later recovered undamaged (*Ibis*, 1941, p. 311).

Noll (*Orn. Beobacht.*, 1955, pp. 82-91) gives the white owl's diet as 99 per cent mammals in Germany, basing his analysis on one year's examination of pellets.

This rather confirms the idea that mammals who squeak are more easily taken by using sound, than birds who are silent at night.

They will also take swifts, presumably snatching them when at roost.

The white owl will take up residence in a dovecot and can do great damage to its tenants, but there are cases where pigeons and owl have lived together in perfect amity.

White owls are sometimes luminescent owing to their contact with the poisonous fungus *Armillaria mellea*.[1] Both at Mottisfont and in Suffolk I have seen a slight luminescence on these owls when viewed on a dark night. If an owl strikes a pane of glass this luminescence will transfer to the glass, giving a complete outline of the bird at the moment of striking.

[1] This fungus is highly luminous and is responsible for most luminous wood in Britain. It causes white-rot in hollow trees and house woodwork; it has been suggested that the 'burning bush' of Moses' tradition originated from this fungus.

PLATE II

Hawk Owl

PLATE 12

Saw-whet Owl: 'Too late'

PLATE 13

Little Owl, flying with a long-tailed field mouse

PLATE 14

Barn Owl

PLATE 15

Saw-whet Owl: 'Caught'

PLATE 16

Great Horned Owl and Mocking Bird: 'Well I'm blowed!'

PLATE 17

Great Horned Owl and Mocking Bird: 'Go away!'

PLATE 18

Short-eared Owl in flight

KING VULTURE
Sarcoramphus papa

From *Travels in the Florida Wilderness* by William Bartram:

These birds but seldom appear but when the deserts are set on fire; they are then seen soaring on the wing, gathering from every quarter and gradually approaching the burnt plains where they alight upon the ground yet smoking with hot embers; they gather up the roasted serpents, frogs and lizards, filling their sacks with them; at this time a person may shoot them with pleasure, they not being willing to quit the feast, and indeed seeming to brave all danger.

BLACK VULTURE
Coragyps atratus

Usually a carrion eater but there are many records of young pigs and lambs being taken (Lovell, *Auk*, 1947, p. 131, and *Wilson Bull.*, 1952, p. 48).

McIllhenny (*Auk*, 1939, pp. 472-4) records cases of them attacking and eating skunks in Louisiana; a single vulture will not attack but will wait until several are gathered round the victim.

Figgins (*Auk*, 1923, p. 666) found that these vultures in the neighbourhood of Bird Island, La., were very destructive in some of the heron rookeries and states that 'it is a frequent occurrence to observe a vulture with a struggling young heron dangling from its beak. In regions where cattle raising has replaced the cultivation of rice, the black vulture is credited with considerable damage to the herds by tearing the eyes from calves at the time of birth and instances are cited of a like treatment accorded cows while in a weakened condition. I personally saw one tear the tail from a small pig and was informed that the practice was common.'

Audubon (*Birds of America*, 1840) says of this vulture in Florida, 'I observed them many times devouring young cormorants and herons in the nest.'

SECRETARY BIRD
Sagittarius serpentarius

The secretary bird is unique in striking his victim, whether snake, small bird or mammal, with the pad of his foot—real hard smacks; they are also peculiar in running into flight and also running after alighting; unlike other hawks, food is always carried in the bill.

They usually hunt in pairs, some little distance apart. They hunt by walking through grass; when a victim is found, the wings are spread, not for protection, but for balance and no doubt to screen the victim. When snakes are attacked the wings are always opened but not used as a shield, for the attack is invariably frontal. I have never seen a secretary bird turn its out-stretched wing to a snake as does the ground hornbill. When attacking a snake there is no hesitation; the snake is struck at once. Snakes are slow to appreciate danger; the only quick-minded snake I know is the mamba, but I can find no record of this hawk attacking a mamba. Moreover, a secretary bird can jump at least six feet into the air with ease, thus avoiding the strike of a snake. There is one record (Stark and Sclater, III, p. 406) of the death of this hawk from snake-bite.

At Naivasha in Kenya I saw a secretary bird lift a large snake some fifty feet into the air and let it drop, then descend and continue smacking it.

In Kenya I saw this hawk kill a four-foot puff adder, a very slow snake, in a few seconds, tear its head off and then leisurely pull the body to pieces and eat it. In all cases of attacks on snakes, the head is not eaten. This was con-firmed many years ago when I arrived at the London Zoo with four grass snakes and was allowed to turn them out before a secretary bird. Each snake was struck eight or ten times in rapid succession with wings out for balance and buoyancy, and with head and neck thrown back. The snakes were then pulled to pieces and swallowed in small morsels, but in every case the head and about an inch of the neck was refused.

Near Middelburg (Cape) I saw a full-grown hare taken in long grass; killing was by smacking hard, blows in quick succession; here again the head was left untouched. Near Nanyuki in Kenya I saw this hawk run after a leveret, half flying and half running with outstretched wings, the small animal constantly stopping and crouching, but eventually succumbing to a hard smack.

The stomach contents of three secretary birds consisted of:

1. Rhodesia. Two snakes less their heads, several grasshoppers and four lizards.
2. Kenya. A small land tortoise, a rodent, three fledgling Passerine birds and many beetles and grasshoppers.

3. Kenya. Stuffed with grasshoppers, beetles. One small lizard and one button quail (*Turnix*).

The secretary bird is easily bullied into giving up its prey. I have seen the bateleur rob it of a snake and have seen a buzzard drive one off a hare.

The secretary bird has good table manners. On the shores of Lake Naivasha I was watching a marsh harrier feeding when a secretary bird walked up to within a few yards, stood gazing at the harrier for about a minute and then turned away; the harrier, alarmed by my presence, flew off with his food which proved to be too heavy and was dropped not twenty yards from the secretary bird who with great dignity walked towards it, inspected it and then with equal dignity walked away again without touching it.

A grass fire will attract secretary birds, who search for scorched rodents, snakes and lizards.

The young are fed almost entirely on grasshoppers and locusts with occasional lizards and pieces of rodents.

BLACK-SHOULDERED KITE
Elanus caeruleus

Many hunts observed in India, Arabia and Africa. Food usually small rodents, small birds, lizards and insects but the colony on Masira Island on the south coast of Arabia have developed a taste for fish.

They hunt by hover, dropping with wings high over the back, hover again and so on until victim is seized and bitten in neck or head.

BAT BUZZARD
Machaerhamphus alcinus

This hawk is widely distributed in Africa but seldom seen owing to its crepuscular, almost nocturnal habits. It feeds almost entirely on bats, moths and small birds coming to roost such as swallows and martins. I have seen them hunting at Kisumu and Mombasa. My first introduction was in Kisumu when searching a large-leafed tree for green pigeon. I saw this small black hawk, about the size of a small buzzard, with white throat and a tuft of elongated feathers on the nape, very large eyes and mouth half-open, giving it a nightjar appearance; it remained in that tree all day but flew out just after sunset and commenced to catch bats and moths in the air, grasping them with its feet, feeding them straight into its mouth and swallowing them whole without dismemberment. The flight was fast and irregular with constant stoops, side-slips and circling. The hawk continued feeding until light failed. On the following morning the hawk was back in his tree.

I came across the bird again in Mombasa where they spent the day in cracks in the old fort, coming out at dusk to feed on birds coming to roost and bats; here again hunting continued until light failed and both birds and bats were swallowed whole.

It has been recorded that as many as eleven bats and ten birds have been found in the stomachs of seven birds.

HONEY BUZZARD
Pernis apivorus

The main diet is the larvae and adults of Hymenoptera, occasionally the pupae of ants and occasionally pheasants (Igalffy, *Larus*, 1948, p. 138), small birds and mammals. Worms and snails have also been recorded.

When stationed in Cologne in 1924 I made friends with a gamekeeper on whose beat were a pair of goshawk and a pair of honey buzzard. On visiting the nest of the latter I was surprised to see the amount of pellets on the ground below the tree; these pellets were quite unlike those of other hawks; they resembled small necklaces of sheep dung strung together by some glutinous substance with a slight admixture of a fine dark fur and remains of insects. One of these pellets was six inches long. Later in the day I subjected some of these pellets to heat and produced melted wax.

At the same place I had a good opportunity to observe a pair of adults excavating wasps' nests, tearing away grass and earth with wonderful rapidity, using one leg at a time and catching wasps as they came out; this was done with great accuracy and rapidity. So engrossed were these birds in their excavation that I was able to get within about twenty yards of them. The wasps' nest was about fifteen inches in and when this was reached they both gorged on pupae, their bills becoming much fouled by wax and debris. During the whole proceeding a cloud of wasps concentrated on the birds, many settling on the head, neck and legs but there was no irritation apparent on the part of the birds.

The middle claw of the honey buzzard is beautifully hollowed out and forms an ideal scraper.

Does the honey buzzard get stung? The feathers on the face are stiff and coarse; it has been doubted whether they offer protection against the sting of a wasp. This sting when fully protruded does not exceed $2\frac{1}{2}$ mm. and that of a hornet 3 mm. The weight of a wasp makes no impression on these short stiff feathers, and they are so arranged that no wasp sitting on them could possibly reach the skin.

In Africa the nest of the virulent wasp *Polybioides* is raided, but the protruded sting is no larger than that of the hornet.

It has been estimated that a single bird will kill 90,000 wasps in the season.

The honey buzzard bred in Britain in 1957. I knew the owner of the estate and the keeper; I was able to arrange complete protection from all kinds of disturbance. But both owner and keeper said 'What about my pheasants?' To satisfy them I said honey buzzards did not molest pheasants, but if this pair did I would reward them 2s. 6d. a pheasant. The wretched birds took forty-seven pheasants. I also put up notices at the entrances to the wood 'Unexploded bombs, keep out.' It certainly kept people out but I got into trouble with the War Office for 'alarming the public.' This particular pair of honey buzzard reared three young who first took wing in late July. In addition to pheasants, the parents were seen on plough searching for insects and the remains of snails were found beneath the nest and in pellets. A pair of sparrowhawks reared four young but forty yards from the honey buzzards.

MEXICAN BLACK HAWK
Urubutinga anthracina

Rarely takes birds, usually frogs, fish, snakes and land crabs. Thomas (*Condor*, 1908, pp. 116-18) records that in parts of Honduras land crabs are their sole diet, 'catching and killing more than they can eat.' Other food includes lizards, snakes and rarely birds.

MISSISSIPPI KITE
Ictinia mississippiensis

Food almost entirely the larger insects, lizards, snakes and sometimes frogs. Birds are not molested and have no fear of this hawk.

SWALLOW-TAILED KITE
Elanoides forficatus

Food is mainly small reptiles, amphibians and insects; small mammals or birds are seldom molested. Nearly all food is obtained and eaten on the wing but they will fly close over the ground, alighting for a moment to take a small snake, lizard or frog; they have also been seen in flocks of two to three hundred pursuing a swarm of bees.

EVERGLADE KITE
Rostrhamus sociabilis

Murphy (*Auk*, 1955, p. 204) describes the feeding habits of this fascinating bird.

The kite darts and skims about over the pools and their shores, and, after spying a snail, it grasps it in one foot and at once flies to a perch. The period of hunting is usually late afternoon or at some other hour when the sun glare is reduced. It is then that the snails move about most, and crawl from the water on to the stems of the low vegetation.

The kite must have a perch to enjoy the fruits of its search. It sits on one foot and holds the snail gently in the other, doing nothing that would inhibit the mollusk from emerging from the whorl of the shell. The bird makes no effort to obtain its food by force; it waits for the voluntary extension of the animal beyond the aperture. When that happens, the bird quickly pierces the snail behind the operculum, always in the same place which is evidently a nerve plexus.

The kite then sits and waits again, with the snail spiked on its maxilla, from which it stands out like a bump as large as the bird's head. Gradually the muscles of the numbed snail relax. After two minutes, more or less, the kite vigorously shakes its head and swallows the mollusk whole, operculum and all, before the empty shell has reached the ground.

The fragile shell is never broken or abraded by the captor. The long, slender bill is used not as a hook but as a lancet or poniard. It is a feat of instinctive correlation as exact as that of the spider-paralyzing wasps.

BLACK KITE AND RED KITE
Milvus migrans and *Milvus milvus*

The black kite is mainly a thief and scavenger, in many towns in the East doing excellent sanitary service. They have a particularly accurate flight, helped by the balance of their forked tail, and will pick small morsels from the ground or water and even from soldiers' plates on the verandahs of barrack rooms. Smaller morsels are devoured in the air but larger ones taken to a tree or rock. Chapin (*B. Belg. Congo*, 1932, p. 559) records the pulp of the oil palm being eaten.

In Lucknow, where many of these kites attended the barrack rooms, snatching food thrown to them on the ground, I tied a thin cord to a dainty morsel with a small model aeroplane at the end. Down came a kite, seized the morsel and went up with it, followed by the little plane. His pace increased when he found this small object following him, he turned in circles, performed all sorts of aerobatics, finally banking and attacking his tormentor; but the tormentor turned with him, still in pursuit. It ended in a tree in which the kite took refuge, and the cord, becoming entangled, pulled the morsel from the kite's grasp.

K. Eates (*epist.*, Oct. 1957) records a remarkable case of piracy by the black kite at Fyzabad in India; it showed remarkable intelligence. An Indian wearing a white cap approached the Post Office, when a kite swooped down and picked it off his head. A few days later Mr Eates heard a kite calling near his kitchen and, looking up, saw the bird had a white cap in its talons; the bird circled Mr Eates's kitchen and out came the cook with some pieces of meat which he threw into the air. The kite dropped the cap and took the meat in the air, eating it as he circled round. The cook told Mr Eates that he had been collecting caps from these kites for several weeks and showed Mr Eates a dozen caps thus secured. Any caps too old or dirty were thrown away but those in good condition were sold. When this particular pair of kites bred and had youngsters to feed, the stealing of caps became more frequent as more and more meat was required. So well known became this habit in Fyzabad that visitors to the Post Office invariably removed their caps when approaching the building.

Pitman (*epist.*) records: 'In Northern Rhodesia, a European Police Inspector with a ruddy shiny bald head, whilst walking hatless near Broken Hill, was savagely attacked by a black kite which had mistaken his red head for meat. The Inspector's head was badly lacerated.'

F. A. C. Munns (*Field*, 31 Oct. 1957) records the black kite snatching a cheroot from a man's mouth, removing a slice of ham from a plate on the table and carrying off a silver toast-rack containing toast.

The kite is a great eater of locusts and flying termites, devouring them in the air after discarding the wings; they will also take small chickens from the ground, rats and voles. They will rob other birds such as hawks smaller than themselves and gulls, of food; even a peregrine was driven from his prey by one of these pirates.

Pitman (*epist.*) records the black kite at dusk in Uganda endeavouring to catch small bats as they emerged from beneath a roof, but with small success. And again the *Ann. Report Uganda Game Dept.*, 1928, p. 35, records them snatching small fish swimming near the surface on Lake Victoria. At Port Sudan I have seen this same kite snatching small fish from the surface near an anchored steamer. J. H. Beesley (*Bull. B.O.C.*, 1956, p. 108) records the African race (*parasitus*) snatching fish four or five inches long from water.

The black kite is more parasitic than the red kite, in Europe and Africa regularly robbing other birds of their prey. In the Sudan I have seen four of these kites harrying an Egyptian vulture until it had to drop its piece of carrion, which was caught in the air as it dropped. And in Europe they will regularly take magpies, poultry and partridges.

EUROPEAN GOSHAWK
Accipiter gentilis

The goshawk, formerly abundant in Britain but now a rare breeding species, extends throughout the Holarctic Region.

I have had good opportunities of watching goshawk in Sweden, Estonia, Germany and Sussex. Two methods of hunting are employed—still-hunting

PLATE 19

Red Kite

and surprise grab in flight. I think still-hunting is the usual method, for the goshawk does not come into the open as much as the sparrowhawk.

I have seen the goshawk kill on five occasions and have not yet seen an unsuccessful hunt.

No bird comes amiss to the goshawk, from capercailzie to tits; also small foxes, wild cat and rodents. Sulkava (*Suom. Riista*, 1956, x, pp. 44-62) records woodland game birds as the main diet of ten pair of goshawk in Finland during the breeding season.

In Germany I found them quite common in the forests of Hanover (1897) and again round Cologne (1925), where their main food is game birds, pigeon and hares with frequent raids on farmyards.

The first kill I witnessed was near Cologne when a male goshawk flew out of conifer forest and intercepted a cuckoo crossing some rough land; the cuckoo turned on seeing the hawk but was quickly overtaken, despite many twists and turns, killed by grasp and carried back into the forest.

The second kill was in Estonia when I was walking through tall conifer forest. A female goshawk suddenly left a tree, gliding steeply and at tremendous speed. She did not appear to check pace until there was an audible bump in the undergrowth of heather and blaeberry and then a furious beating of wings and feathers flying in all directions. I ran towards the spot and found a large hen capercailzie stone dead with its neck torn out and all the vertebrae punctured by the hawk's claws. This must have caused almost instantaneous death. We left the carcase for the goshawk as they always return to their kill after disturbance.

The third kill occurred a few days later. On still autumn evenings it was the custom of goshawk from the forests of northern Estonia to take an evening flight, making use of thermal up-currents. As many as seven have been seen in the air at one time. On this particular evening there were five goshawk in the air and about 1,500 feet up, with several hooded crows accompanying them and annoying them. Quite suddenly a goshawk side-slipped, clutched a crow for perhaps ten seconds, dropped him and continued his soar in the evening sun. The crow was dead when I picked him up.

Soon afterwards in the same place I saw my fourth kill—again a crow. A single goshawk was soaring over a bog and was soon joined by a noisy crowd of crows. The hawk was supremely indifferent until their attentions bored him, when he suddenly turned, put on speed and in the twinkling of an eye

G

seized and killed two crows which fell to the ground one after the other, both stone dead, having been punctured in the neck by the claws. Having vented his feelings on the crows he sailed off, the rest of the crows descending to earth to hold a loud post-mortem on their comrades.

The fifth occasion was in Sussex in deep beech wood during the breeding season. I was sitting down hoping to see goshawk when quite suddenly there was a scurry close to me and a male goshawk was chasing a woodpigeon in and out of tree-trunks and under the leaf ceiling. It was a wonderful exhibition of aerobatics, somersaults and upside-downs. Twice I saw the hawk stretch out a foot to grab, the pigeon escaping by a side-slip. The pigeon was eventually knocked off balance by the hawk's wing and was at once seized by both feet and taken to the ground, where the hawk sat on his victim for perhaps two minutes before commencing to feed, the first act of which was plucking.

I believe the main food of the breeding goshawk in Sussex is woodpigeon and hen pheasant.

In parts of Europe they become a serious menace to both game and poultry if not kept in check. It is recorded that a sportsman shot a brace of partridge and whilst reloading 'something passed close by my ear with the rush of a whirlwind and on looking up I saw a goshawk in the act of pouncing on one of my birds that was lying dead within thirty paces of where I stood, and which it bore away in its talons.'

There are also recorded cases of goshawk following sportsmen in forest when shooting blackgame or capercailzie, and snatching shot birds.

Kramer (*Wittenberg Lutherstadt*, 1955) gives the main food of goshawks as jays, tame pigeons, partridges and woodpigeons, with small birds as small as sparrows.

Küchler (*Beitr. z. Vogelkunde*, 1958, pp. 310-11) records a goshawk seizing a duck off the water.

As boys, my brother and I used to stay at Lilford in Northamptonshire. Once a week the falconer would take us out with three trained goshawk searching for rabbits and moorhen for the captive hawks and owls in Lord Lilford's aviaries. We never saw a miss; every hunt was successful. The rabbits were overtaken in a flash, and if there was any struggle the goshawk would catch hold of grass or bracken with one leg in order to hold the rodent whilst the falconer would come up and give the bird a tit-bit, and then

PLATE 20

Goshawk and Gazelle

another hunt.[1] The moorhen were taken over water, a keeper tapping the reeds by the side of the river and so soon as a moorhen scurried across to the other bank the hawk was unleashed, quickly overtook its prey and bore it to dry land. The moorhen was always quite dead, its neck vertebrae being pierced by grasp. Goshawks, especially females, have a very powerful grip, so much so that when it seizes a rabbit or hare by the head with one foot, the victim is dead almost at once.

Goshawks are amazingly persistent when hunting; in pursuit they will follow prey through the thickest trees or bushes and once they bind to their prey they never release hold. A rabbit caught by the hind quarters as it was entering its burrow has been known to drag the goshawk into the hole so that the bird had to be dug out.

Trained goshawk have been entered to gazelle in India, the hawk binding to the animal's head, flustering it and enabling greyhounds to catch up and pull it down. Even the wild ass is said to be not immune from this combination of hawk and hound (*Falconry in the Valley of the Indus*, 1852, pp. 83-4).

AMERICAN GOSHAWK
Accipiter atricapillus

Much the same killing habits as its European representative. Audubon (*Birds of America*, 1840) records a goshawk attacking a flock of blackbirds (*Quiscalus*), flying into the flock and seizing one, then another and another until he had five down in the water below him; these he subsequently retrieved, carrying each separately to the shore. But Audubon is not always accurate.

Forbush (*Birds of Massachusetts*, 1927) records this goshawk as following a hen 'into a kitchen and seized it on the kitchen floor in the presence of an old man and his daughter. The father beat off the hawk with a cane while the daughter closed the door and finally killed the bird. On another occasion a goshawk caught a half-grown hen which escaped and ran under a woman's skirt, the hawk following right up to the skirt and was killed.'

There are also several records of female goshawk attacking and wounding men who approached their nest (*Bent. Bull. U.S. Nat. Mus.*, 1937, p. 135).

[1] Goshawks do not always clutch grass when they bind to a struggling quarry.

SPARROWHAWK

Accipiter nisus

A resident Palaearctic species from Ireland to Japan and extending south to North Africa and northern India.

A very active bird with two distinct methods of hunting—still-hunting and surprise attack from very low elevations. Prey consists of small mammals from the size of red squirrels downwards and all species of birds from grouse, partridges and curlew to the smaller birds. It is remarkable how very seldom the robin is taken, and there is, so far as I can ascertain, no record of a wren in a sparrowhawk's diet, though, as related below, attempts have been made. On the other hand there is a record of a sparrowhawk being taken by his own kind and they are frequently taken by peregrine and goshawk.

A marked characteristic of the sparrowhawk's technique is its ability to fly at about 40 miles an hour through bush country and suddenly turn at right angles and snap up some unsuspecting victim. To be able to dodge branches and at the same time locate a small bird shows remarkable accuracy in flight and vision.

In Britain sparrowhawks will pursue their victim into the thickest hedges, even blackthorn, rose and holly, often damaging themselves. I have picked out two long blackthorn spikes from the breast of a male sparrowhawk.

There are many records of sparrowhawks taking jays. Female sparrowhawks average about 250 grammes in weight and jays about 170 to 185 grammes, and the jay has a formidable bill, so it is no mean feat on the hawk's part.

When we lived at Mottisfont we kept records over a period of ten years of successful hunts by sparrowhawks, information by keepers being included. Victims comprised,

22 linnets	1 green woodpecker
19 chaffinches	3 thrushes
7 greenfinches	2 partridges
14 house sparrows	3 young pheasants
1 tree sparrow	1 water rail
8 yellow-hammers	11 woodpigeon
2 reed buntings	1 stock dove
1 spotted flycatcher	2 redwing

10 skylarks	1 meadow pipit
7 jays	8 starling
1 goldfinch	1 whitethroat

It will be seen that farmyard and hedgerow birds predominate.

Since 1903 I have personally seen in the British Isles seventeen successful hunts including,

1 green woodpecker	3 yellow-hammers
1 stock dove	1 young cuckoo
7 starlings	1 song thrush
2 sparrows	1 twite

The immunity of tits, tree-creepers, nuthatches, robins and wrens is remarkable; nor do these victims appear much in literature. Robins have only been recorded as victims when on migration and away from their usual habitat, and I have no record of a wren being taken, though I once saw in Cornwall an unsuccessful hunt in stone-wall country. A wren suddenly bobbed up with his challenging paean of self-satisfaction which soon altered to the *tic-tic* of alarm as he saw a sparrowhawk flying low in his direction. Down popped the wren into the loose stones and the hawk settled on the wall exactly where the wren had vanished. Up popped the wren not ten feet from the hawk, another *tic-tic*, and he was gone again before the hawk moved. Another pop-up, this time about ten yards from the hawk, another *tic-tic* and back into the wall. The hawk realised the game and made off. But the troglodyte was not satisfied with such an ending. He popped up for the last time to celebrate the victory, pouring out his soul in a paean of superiority and contempt for all predators.

A. A. Smith (*Field*, 2 Aug. 1956) records the remains of twenty-eight birds being found round a nest of young sparrowhawks, the victims being mainly finches, together with hedge sparrows, tits and a blackbird, the bodies being partially plucked but untouched by the young.

Kramer (*Wittenberg Lutherstadt*, 1955) gives the main food of sparrowhawks as sparrows, thrushes, bullfinches, skylarks and small rodents in Germany, and argues that the species is deserving of protection.

I doubt if individual sparrowhawks have preferences in food. I agree with Tinbergen (*Ardea*, 1946, pp. 12-13) that they take whatever comes their way with the least trouble, but a comparison of the food with the bird population of the district does not show that the different species are represented pro-portionally. A sparrowhawk's food is usually taken from species feeding away from cover, the victim being caught in the open.

Rudebeck (*Oikos*, 1950), whose observations are almost entirely taken in the Baltic during migration, records 190 hunts of which 23 only were successful. He records the rare prolonged stoop with folded wings which was invariably unsuccessful (p. 79); a dive into a flock of starlings when a victim was seized (p. 83); the capture of robins on migration (p. 82); an account of a merlin and sparrowhawk after the same swallow in two cases and in each the merlin failed (p. 83); a sparrowhawk stalking a bird using a man—himself—as a stalking horse, the hawk actually touching his field glasses as it passed him (p. 84); and only a single attack on migrating woodpigeon.

Rudebeck (p. 87) records 60 out of the 190 hunts being directed against migrating flocks, and only in five cases was the hunt successful.

After reading Rudebeck, Tinbergen and others, combined with others' and my own observations, there is little doubt that the sparrowhawk will select a defective or laggard bird when a preference exists, the slowest of the flock or the most timid who loses its head and falls out, or the slowest mover; its influence is therefore selective and beneficial.

A female sparrowhawk can carry birds even heavier than itself. I have a record of one weighing 294 grammes carrying a partridge weighing 378 grammes, and another female weighing 246 grammes carrying a stock dove of 368 grammes. By carrying I mean becoming air-borne over a distance of a few yards.

In Arabia I was watching a hoopoe 'hup-hupping' on top of a tree with crest depressed and his lady below. A sparrowhawk gliding down the wadi suddenly turned in their direction with evil intent. The hoopoes reacted like lightning. They both dived like rockets into the heart of a thorn bush; the hawk, appreciating defeat, passed on, but it was a good ten minutes before those two hoopoe recovered their composure.

Campbell (*Brit. B.*, 1949, p. 24) records a hoopoe being attacked by a sparrowhawk in Ireland. The hoopoe took refuge under a gate with the hawk sitting on the gate. The hoopoe foolishly flew off and after four un-successful attacks was killed. The hoopoe was of course a straggler in a strange country. Hoopoe in their own country are by no means easy victims though their brilliant plumage invariably attracts predators.

PLATE XX

PLATE 21

Sparrowhawk and Starling

Near our camp in Afghanistan was a large flock of tree sparrows. It was in spring when an incredible number of sparrowhawks of two species (*nisus* and *badius*) were on passage. When not feeding the sparrows had two refuges, the one in a tall poplar and the other in a dense rose bush, this latter being hawk-proof. I was watching the sparrows sitting on the leafless poplar when they suddenly dived into the rose-bush and in their wake came a cock sparrowhawk, just too late for success. He sat on the ground beside the rose bush, tried to force an entrance but failed. By this time the sparrows were deep down in the centre of the bush. A second cock sparrowhawk arrived on the scene, no doubt attracted by the loud twittering of the sparrows. This second hawk made a headlong charge against the rose-bush, the sparrows shrieked murder and were near on losing their heads. Both hawks now flew round the bush trying to find an entrance; the sparrows were rapidly reaching the end of their endurance to this ordeal, and thinking they might do something really foolish I intervened, for I am fond of tree sparrows. Those little sparrows must have several similar experiences every day so no wonder their nerves were on edge.

I witnessed an interesting kill in Gloucestershire when a green woodpecker was flying from one wood to another over a lake about half a mile across. When half-way across a female sparrowhawk came out to meet it. The yaffle yaffled, turned and fled back to cover. The hawk followed, rapidly overtook the slow undulating flight of the victim, dipped below the bird and clutched from below, the yaffling stopped at once and the victim was borne off to the wood. I have seen starlings taken in similar fashion, grasped from below.

In the winter of 1905–6 I was living in Hampshire close to a large starling roost. Every evening as regular as clockwork a hen sparrowhawk would select and capture a starling. She always launched her attack from the same branch of the same tree and the procedure was always the same. Selecting a bird slightly above her she would engage in a follow-chase of about fifty yards, turn on her back and seize the victim from below, returning to her branch to feed. We never saw her attack in the mornings when the starlings went out, but so regular and so entertaining was the evening hunt that she was spared the usual fate of her kind.

In Ross-shire I have witnessed a deliberate attack by a female sparrowhawk on a cock capercailzie caught in the open. I was sitting in a belt of conifer when I spied a cock caper in long heather and about twenty yards from cover.

93

A female sparrowhawk swooped down on him but did not strike; the caper fluffed out his head and neck to strike a ferocious attitude; but the hawk was not impressed. The hawk made repeated stoops, the caper always turning to face the impertinence; his hackles stood out, his tail was fanned out and erect, but he kept well down in the heather as his tormentor ragged him without once touching him. When the sparrowhawk tired of his game, the caper, his dignity shaken, scuttled back to cover quite close to me and took pains to rearrange his ruffled plumage and nerves.

There are several records of attacks on the red squirrel, the hawk chasing them round trunks of trees and through dense foliage but seldom with success. Ellis (*Brit. B.*, 1940, p. 248) records two female sparrowhawks attacking a red squirrel, but they got in each others' way and the squirrel escaped.

In Suffolk I have seen the red-legged partridge take refuge down rabbit holes when threatened by a sparrowhawk, and in Caithness I have seen a covey of grouse take refuge in a corn stook, the hawk sitting on top with head on one side and not quite understanding such unconventional evasion.

One of the most remarkable kills I have witnessed was in Arabia. I was walking up quail and a female sparrowhawk was sitting on a cactus hedge near by. A flushed quail topped the hedge where the hawk sat, passing within about a foot of it. The hawk seized the quail in flight but was thrown off balance by the impact of 100 grammes travelling thirty miles an hour, and fell to the ground, soon recovered herself and flew off for the meal.

Another remarkable achievement by a cock sparrowhawk was seen in Wiltshire. I was walking up a hedge and in front of me was a busy party of long-tailed tits. When the hedge came to an end this party had to fly over an open field. No sooner did they embark than the hawk appeared, soon over-took them, grabbed first one then another and flew off with a brace of unfortunates.

At Hufoof in Arabia I saw a sparrowhawk make a smash-and-grab raid after Spanish sparrows cowering in a tangle of barbed wire; the hawk was so injured and lacerated that it was unable to fly and had to be killed.

Gordon Turnill (*epist.*, 26 Sept. 1957) records a sparrowhawk coming down on a 'set-up' woodpigeon immediately after a shot and trying to carry it off.

Mrs Cowdy (*epist.*) records a sparrowhawk seizing blue tits when feeding on a bird table; and Tutt (*Field*, 2 July 1956) records many cases of sparrow-hawks raiding nests of small Passerines and eating chicks.

D. Martin (*Field*, 22 Aug. 1957) records a common sandpiper diving when chased by a sparrowhawk. (See also under marsh harrier.) Lord Leven (*epist.*) records a sparrowhawk eating another of its own species which had just been shot by his keeper. Mrs Upton (*epist.*) records one entering an aviary of Liberty budgerigars in Essex, killing and eating one and then attacking a second.

I have made several enquiries from owners and gamekeepers on large estates in Britain, asking for the number of pairs of sparrowhawks per square mile. The result averaged out at one pair for every 25 to 30 square miles. The total square mileage of Britain (including Scotland) is 88,700, of which about 80,000 is suitable sparrowhawk country. That works out at from 2,600 to 3,200 pairs or, say, 5,800 individuals, which means that about 12,000 small birds are killed daily by sparrowhawks in Britain. For the year, that works out at the sad total of well over four million birds; and even so, small hedgerow and woodland birds are still abundant in Britain. N. Zambra (*Field*, 23 Oct. 1958) boasts that he had killed 71 in 1947. The harm this little hawk does is negligible and the pleasure it gives to many of us is considerable.

Before leaving the sparrowhawk I must introduce a small male bird, reared from the nest, very red underneath and christened Lazybones, as he was quite the most indolent hawk I ever met. He was never hooded nor jessed and was ridiculously tame. We only flew him in farmyards and around ricks after sparrows, finches and the like. He refused to fly more than about thirty yards but was amazingly successful once he got started. We would take him up to about ten yards from feeding birds and he would go like a rocket, seldom missing. He would sit on the victim, refusing to feed unless we commenced plucking. My brother and I, still at school, took him to London and introduced him to the innocent sparrows then—over sixty years ago—abundant in Hyde Park. He never failed against the London sparrow. The park-keepers could find no law about hawking in the Royal Park and it was not until my father had a letter from some high authority that our effort at falconry in a Royal Park ceased.

THE AFRICAN SPARROWHAWKS
Accipiter minullus, rufiventris and *melanoleucus*

I have seen these three sparrowhawks hunting and their technique varies little from that of the European sparrowhawks.

My first introduction to *minullus* was in some forest near the mouth of the Gamtoos River (its type locality). Its small size enables it to dash at great speed through thick foliage trees and small Passerines run a poor chance once this little hawk has chosen its victim. It adopts both still- and chase-hunting, usually in or on the fringe of forest or thick bush and on the three occasions on which I have witnessed a kill, the victim was taken to a tree for the meal.

I have seen *rufiventris* hunting but have never witnessed a kill; flying quite close to the ground in and out of thick trees, this species no doubt employs the same technique as its relatives—surprise attacks on any small bird caught in the open or on the fringe of forest or bush.

I have frequently seen *melanoleucus* hunting. Their large size make them appear less active than most sparrowhawks. Near Nairobi I saw one, flying low over grass, suddenly perform a marvellous right-about turn and snatch a Delagorgue's quail which was taken to a near-by tree for eating. This was the commonest sparrowhawk round Fort Hall and Nyeri in Kenya when I was stationed there fifty-five years ago and was often seen a long way from trees or bush. I witnessed several unsuccessful hunts, two after shrikes in thorn bush and one after a wheatear which vanished down a hole. The Kikuyu regard it as a great danger to poultry.

Their main food is doves which they will follow-chase for up to two miles, chasing them out of trees.

They have a curious technique when hunting tame pigeons on a farm near Nanyuki; when the hawk appears the pigeon circles round its loft, the hawk doing smaller circles in the opposite direction; when the two circles converge the hawk accelerates and tries to grab the pigeon; this takes place about a hundred feet up and when the pigeon tires of the game it dives into its dovecot and the hawk clears off.

BESRA SPARROWHAWK
Accipiter virgatus

Only seen hunting twice, on each occasion in the Himalayas and in both cases in fairly thick forest, the method employed being still-hunting, the victim being seized after a rapid descent from a tree; in one case the victim was a laughing thrush (*Garrulax*) and in the other a small bird whose identity I never ascertained.

PLATE 22

Cooper's Hawk

LEVANT SPARROWHAWK
Accipiter badius

See under Sparrowhawk when a mixed party of *A. nisus* and *badius* were hunting tree sparrows in Afghanistan.

In Africa I have seen the race *sphenurus* raiding community-nesting weaver birds and glossy starlings but with varying success. Out of six attacks seen, only one was successful.

In Arabia near Jedda I saw a female *brevipes* make an attempt on a greater spotted cuckoo, both turning and twisting and side-slipping in the air, the victim finally reaching a thick-foliaged tree when the hawk gave up. The hawk was on passage.

COOPER'S HAWK
Accipiter cooperi

Food and hunting much the same as European *Accipiters;* a great poultry raider, as many as fifty chickens being taken from a single farm, twelve of which were taken in a single day; they also take the smallest birds and mammals ranging from hares to mice. Savage (*Western Orn.*, 1900, pp. 6-8) records this hawk chasing a quail, shooting beneath it, turning on its back and seizing the quail from below. There are also records of this hawk attacking kingfishers which escape by diving. A. A. Saunders (*epist.*) records this hawk sitting and watching a flicker (*Colaptes*) on a grassy hill-side. The flicker tried to hop away from the hawk but was seized and brought back, released and the hawk retired to watch again. This went on several times, 'the hawk apparently playing with the flicker. Finally the hawk seized the flicker and flew off.'

SHARP-SHINNED HAWK
Accipiter velox

Food ranges from poultry to insects and hunting is much the same as that of the European sparrowhawk. Maynard (*B. Eastern N. America*) records one pouncing on a night heron in flight, both birds falling to the ground, when the heron gave such a loud squark that the hawk abandoned its prey and fled.

THE CHANTING AND GABAR GOSHAWKS

Melierax gabar, metabates and *musicus*

The chanting goshawks do not chant nor have they any song as recounted by Levaillant; the call note is more like a rasping flute than any resemblance to the human chant.

I have seen all three species hunting, including the northern race—*poliopterus* —from Somaliland. I do not think they touch carrion; corpses of birds laid out for them remained untouched in Arabia. When not hunting the flight is almost lazy but of great speed when in pursuit or stalking; they will follow prey into thick bush, and the small *gabar* followed a dove into my room in Somaliland, which resulted in both birds becoming specimens.

Gabar will also raid colonies of weaver birds and glossy starlings, snatching birds as they go in or come out of their nests; but in Somaliland I saw starlings combine in driving the hawk off. Also in Somaliland I saw *gabar* threaten a party of eight ox-peckers (*Buphagus*) in a bush. The ox-peckers retired into the centre of the bush, swearing, but *gabar* was determined, followed them in, drove them out and caught one on the wing. But most hunting is still-hunting from a convenient perch in a tree or from a telegraph post.

I have seen *metabates* hunting in Morocco, Yemen and in northern Kenya. Main food lizards, chameleons and grasshoppers. I have watched an unsuccessful hunt after pigeon and many successful snatches at rodents, lizards and babblers. In Arabia a pair nested alongside a watering-place for sandgrouse and never once were the latter molested. They are quick to spot a wounded bird and do so under the eyes of the shooter. Near Aden I wounded a grackle, the bird falling in the open; I went to pick it up when *metabates* forestalled me by snatching it within a few feet of me.

At Birka in Arabia at the end of March I watched a pair building their nest in a large tree. Towards evening several ravens (*ruficollis*) would try to rag the hawks as they played around before retiring, but they took good care to avoid close quarters. One raven, bolder than the rest, hopped into the tree close to the hawk; the latter, reacting instantly to the impertinence, clutched the raven by the hind leg and then loosened its hold; that put a stop to ragging.

On another occasion in Arabia, one of these goshawks swung past me at great speed at a downward angle. She crashed into sand; I just caught a glimpse of a small fat rodent disappearing into a hole; the hawk sat for a moment, looking dazed and apparently conscious of failure, then flew back to her tree and again watched the hole. After about twenty minutes, out popped the little rodent and commenced feeding. This time there was no error. Like a flash the goshawk was down on him, sat for a moment, then carried him off out of sight.

In Nyasaland I have seen this goshawk tackle a snake in long grass. The hawk descended to the ground and with head feathers erect became intent in watching something I could not see. He stood thus for about ten minutes before he suddenly struck out in front of him and at once became involved in a scuffle which lasted about a minute. He then flew off with a snake about two feet long dangling from his feet and repaired to a tree to eat it.

I have seen *musicus* hunting in South West Africa and its race *poliopterus* in northern Kenya. They appear to prey on larger mammals than does *metabates*, taking hares, francolin and even bustard. Near Windhoek a small bustard, on seeing me, crouched under a small bush. I sat down and watched and as I did so, a goshawk swooped down, landed about fifty feet from the bush and ran like a cock pheasant into the bush where the bustard was; after a very short struggle, all was quiet and the hawk got down to his meal inside the bush.

BUZZARD
Buteo buteo

I have watched many buzzards hunting both in the British Islands and abroad. They have many techniques and a large variety of prey ranging from birds smaller than themselves, hares, rabbits and small rodents, squirrels, fish, insects and earth worms. They have also been noted following the plough for grubs. In Northern Europe they have been known to eat the fruit of the sloe (*Prunus*) and the rose.

Ivkovic (*Larus*, 1949, p. 370) records two chicken, four young missel-thrushes (*Turdus viscivorus*), a mole, two mice and a lizard brought by its parents to the nest of one young buzzard.

They have been seen snatching starlings in the air (*Brit. B.*, 1951, p. 412), and taking tufted duck, coot and moorhen (*Brit. B.*, 1955, p. 326). Adult grouse have no fear of buzzard and in the breeding season, with chicks about, thick heather is sufficient protection; I have never seen a buzzard descend and hunt on foot.

I witnessed a buzzard hunting a squirrel in Ross-shire, the latter being among three isolated Scots pine some forty yards from a large larch plantation; the hawk was flying past and swerved into the pine on seeing the squirrel and sat in one of the trees with the squirrel jabbering excitedly quite close to him; the buzzard would move from branch to branch trying to make the squirrel bolt for the main plantation. After about five minutes of manoeuvring the squirrel decided to make a dash for it, ran to the end of a low bough and took a flying leap into the heather towards the larch. The buzzard was after him in a second, in fact, it was just the manoeuvre he was waiting for, and no doubt he would have caught that squirrel had I not intervened.

In Britain I believe the main food of the buzzard to be rabbits—or *was* rabbits. Before the days of myxomatosis, when rabbits abounded in Scotland, a rabbit-catcher was employed on an estate in Ross-shire. Two pairs of buzzard were resident. The catcher complained that the buzzard were taking the rabbits from his snares. I spent several days watching the buzzards. They would soar around whilst snares were being set and then take up positions whence they could see a rabbit in trouble; the buzzard, sometimes the pair, would then secure the rabbit. It was a lazy game but showed intelligence. At dawn the buzzards would be out patrolling the snared country and robbing the catcher of his rabbits. It was only when I persuaded the rabbit-catcher to get up an hour or two earlier that he got his rabbits intact. We had plenty of buzzard and plenty of rabbits and I prefer the former to the latter.

In Devon I came across a buzzard sitting beside a rolled-up hedgehog. What would have been the outcome I do not know for the hawk flew off at my approach; the hedgehog unrolled and went on his way.

Sandeman (*Brit. B.*, 1952, p. 418) records a buzzard following a hare in Wales for ten minutes, the hare taking refuge in a bush from which the hawk drove it, but the chase was regarded as more play than serious. On two occasions in Ross-shire I have seen buzzard chasing blue hares, flying either close behind them or alongside them, but I never witnessed a kill.

Robinson (*Brit. B.*, 1951, p. 412) records a buzzard snatching a starling from a party of five flying over water in Pembrokeshire.

Buzzards will not only scavenge on dead fish but will snatch living fish from water. I have seen this in Devon and in Karachi Harbour. They will

PLATE 23

European Goshawk

also take eels (Milner, *Field*, 9 June 1955) holding the eel's head in the beak and the body in their claws.

RED-TAILED HAWK
Buteo jamaicensis

Food mainly rodents but a poultry snatcher; hunts by soaring, by low flight and also still-hunting. When hunting squirrels there is seldom success unless they hunt in pairs. Nauman (*Wilson Bull.*, 1929, p. 252) records this buzzard attacking a domestic cat caught out in the open. After a reconnaissance the hawk plunged down into the meadow. 'Instantly there was a mighty commotion. Hissing, flopping, spitting, caterwauling; and one could see feet, claws, wings and tails whirling about just over the grass. The air was full of fur and feathers for a few moments, then the hawk made his getaway and with feathers much ruffled flew for the timber as fast as his wings could carry him. And an old grey tom-cat went with great haste for the farm buildings. Both Tommy and hawk were licked but still able to go.'

F. Barber-Starkey (*epist.*) records one killing and flying off with a sharp-shinned hawk (*Accipiter striatus*).

SWAINSON'S HAWK
Buteo swainsoni

Seeks its prey by soaring and still-hunting and will also follow the plough; a great insect eater, catching and eating them on the wing. They seldom molest birds.

RED-SHOULDERED HAWK
Buteo lineatus

Said to be one of America's most beneficial and least harmful hawks; the diet is varied, including small mammals, birds, snakes, frogs, fish, worms and snails, obtained by still-hunting and gracefully gliding through forest or over meadow land.

GRASSHOPPER BUZZARD-EAGLE
Bustatur rufipennis

This hawk makes little effort, has an abundance of food at hand and appears to spend most of its time resting after a meal. Its diet requires little exertion, comprising locusts, flying termites, small snakes and lizards, small rodents and wounded or sick birds. They are usually seen sitting on a bare branch of a tree or less commonly hunting low over grass country. Even a small locust is attacked as though it were a savage cat—head and neck feathers stuck out, tail and wings spread and everything done to achieve ferocious aggression.

CRESTED HAWK-EAGLE
Lophaëtus occipitalis

Usually seen sitting on telegraph poles and still-hunting, preferably near water, as frogs form a considerable part of the diet; it will also walk slowly beside or in shallow water searching for frogs.

But they will also take feathered game. Near Isiolo I saw one swoop with terrific speed on to a flock of vulturine guineafowl under a thorn tree, but he failed to get one. And in the Nandi country of Kenya I flushed a small francolin, wounded him and he wobbled off with legs dangling. This eagle came up behind me, stooped at great pace and, seizing the francolin, carried him off without a check to a tree.

CROWNED HAWK-EAGLE
Stephanoaëtus coronatus

This magnificent eagle is not known to feed on carrion, its main prey being mammals as large as hyrax, small pigs, cats, lambs, etc., but especially monkeys. When attacking ground animals they descend by steep stoop or will hover stationary before gliding down on to the victim. Killing is instantaneous by grasp, the victim being held by the neck.

Pitman (*Ann. Report Game Dept., Uganda*, 1940, p. 12) records a four-months' baby being snatched by this eagle in the Elgon District of Uganda;

the babe was carried about six yards when it fell out of its clothes which were taken on by the eagle; the babe was not seriously injured.

On two occasions I have seen this eagle chasing monkeys, but each time without success; on the first occasion, near Nyeri in Kenya, a party of colobus was surprised, the eagle dashing into the tree in which they were feeding high up; but the colobus were too active, throwing themselves from bough to bough until they reached safety in a very thick tree where the eagle could not follow; the noise was intense, attracting a party of large hornbill who attempted to mob the eagle.

The second occasion was in the Kabwuren Forest (Nandi), when I heard a terrific commotion from monkeys and saw this eagle dashing about in the tree-tops hard on the heels of a single monkey, the eagle trying to prevent him from descending into thick undergrowth and constantly flying below him; but the monkey eventually plunged down, a direct drop, and landed on a wild banana, whence he scuttled off to join his terrified companions whose jabbering continued for some minutes after the eagle departed.

Capt. Pitman (*epist.*) writes: 'On several occasions I have been able to look down on forest in Uganda and watch this eagle endeavouring to surprise colobus monkeys sunning themselves on the tree-tops. On two occasions I have seen a kill, both young animals; adults are far too quick in making a get-away but some of the younger ones are too terrified to react. In gallery-type forest this eagle will fly rapidly just below tree-tops trying to knock a colobus off a branch. The colobus reaction when thus attacked is to freeze against the trunk of the tree.'

And again: 'In the forest near Entebbe, in the course of investigations with the vectors of yellow fever, a number of monkeys on running-chains were kept on platforms at various heights on the forest trees. Those on the top platforms soon attracted the attention of this eagle who quickly killed the lot.'

A Dutch farmer near the Knysna Forest related to me how a 'great crested eagle' made an unsuccessful attack on a troupe of baboons on his farm, but they managed to concentrate and drove the eagle off 'with grimaces and screams.' The farmer added: 'It reminded me of British infantry forming square to receive Dutch cavalry.' I was not amused.

At Naivasha in Kenya I saw an unsuccessful attack by this eagle on a dik-dik. I was watching the dik-dik from about a hundred yards and had also seen the eagle sitting motionless in a thorn tree above them with head down and watching them. Suddenly the eagle dropped like a stone with wings closed; off went the dik-dik but it was deliberately struck by one wing of the eagle which bowled the little antelope over; the dik-dik recovered at once and made off, the eagle making a grab at it with its powerful leg but failing to strike. He sat there for about a minute and then flew off.

At Marsabit, also in Kenya, I have seen them hovering in rather a clumsy fashion against the wind.

In Rhodesia in 1907 I saw a method by which this eagle tackles a large snake. The reptile was on a small open space, curled up; it was a cobra of sorts as it had a hood. The eagle swooped down and settled about five feet from the cobra who immediately raised its head in a threatening attitude. The eagle watched the snake for over a minute and then, fluffing out all its feathers and half-opening its wings, took a step forward; the snake commenced to sway from side to side with tongue in rapid movement. The eagle watched the snake intently, very slowly and deliberately advancing towards it and looking enormous with all its feathers spread out. When about three feet from the snake, the latter struck out, the eagle throwing back its head but not retreating. Then a slight advance towards the snake and repeated strikes by the latter, each strike becoming less and less vigorous until the eagle was but two feet from the snake, still with all its feathers fluffed out and wings half-spread. The snake, from repeated strikes, soon became exhausted, the strikes became less and less vigorous until finally the eagle made one pounce and grabbed the snake by the head, at once flying off in triumph with its talons encircled by the writhing cobra.

MARTIAL EAGLE
Polemaëtus bellicosus

This large eagle is not known to take carrion. It has been reported killing lambs, goats, steinbok, hares, etc., and has been known to take a jackal, killing it instantaneously with its powerful grasp. The jackal never even made a sound.

I have seen this eagle hunting successfully on two occasions. Once in the Nandi country, when I saw the bird hovering in rather a clumsy manner over

PLATE 24

Golden Eagle

long grass. He suddenly retracted his wings and, stooping at a very steep angle, rose almost at once with a guineafowl, using both feet for the carry. He flew some distance to a tree to feed.

The second occasion was near Marsabit in northern Kenya. I was watching the eagle on a dead branch. He was clearly interested in something, as his head was bobbing and turned slightly to one side. Following his gaze, I saw a female gerenuk with young about a quarter grown. Suddenly the eagle launched his attack, a steep swoop without check on to the baby who collapsed on impact. The mother bolted a few yards but soon turned and came prancing up to the eagle, her forelegs on high; but the eagle raised his hackles, threw out his wings to their full extent and in this threatening attitude faced the mother who dared not approach and finally made off. The young gerenuk was held by both the eagle's legs, claws embedded in the neck; death must have been instantaneous. The first attempt to fly off was not a success, the eagle only succeeding in managing about fifty yards; but at the second attempt on a downward slope he managed to reach a low branch in a tree. There he remained for at least ten minutes before attempting to feed.

Col. Ewart Grogan has recorded to me that he witnessed a large eagle, probably this species, attack and grapple a white stork about 500 feet up; the two fell on his car, the stork striking repeatedly at the eagle with its bill. The struggle continued on the roof of his car and was only brought to an end by both birds being severely beaten with a stick.

Sir Robert Tredgold (verbal communication and letter) records that it was 'almost certainly this eagle which seized a cat near Inyatt and took wing; but the eagle soon descended, releasing the cat which beat a hurried retreat into the house apparently uninjured; the eagle expired having been badly bitten in the throat.'

I have known several cases where cats and puppies have been seized by owls and hawks without damage; this is due, I presume, to the looseness of their skin.

Sir Robert again records an astonishing boldness of behaviour in the same hawk:

About 1928 I was travelling a country road in Rhodesia in an old Ford car. As we passed under a big tree a martial eagle swooped through the tree, collecting on the way a night ape (*Otalemur*). The hawk flew straight down the road in front of us; I worked the old Ford to its maximum speed which was somewhere about

30 m.p.h. After about twenty yards we caught up with the eagle and hit it with the car; the eagle dropped the ape which disappeared under the car undamaged. Halting the car I got out, taking my .22 rifle with me, and found the little ape lying on the road apparently unconscious. Picking it up and holding it for some time, it began to show signs of life. Just then there was a rush of wings and the eagle returned trying to take the ape from my hands. I dropped the ape and struck at the eagle with my rifle which drove him off and as he went I fired at him and missed.

Mr M. P. Stuart Irwin records (*epist.*) a case of this eagle taking a chick of the ostrich in Ngamiland; he came across a pair of ostrich accompanied by eight chicks about ten days old; alarmed by the motor car the adults left the chicks, when a martial eagle swooped down, picked up a chick with both feet and carried it off, struggling hard, to a tree stump. A pair of hawk eagles (*Hieraëtus spilogaster*) appeared and made repeated stoops at the martial eagle, forcing him to come to the ground; the martial eagle finally flew off with his prey, being closely mobbed by the two hawk-eagles. The parent ostriches did not appear to have noticed the loss of one of their brood.

BONELLI'S, BOOTED AND AYRES'S EAGLE
Hieraëtus fasciatus, pennatus and *ayresi*

These three eagles, together with *spilogaster*—a race of *fasciatus*—can be treated together as their habits are identical. I have never known any of these eagles to touch carrion. They all appear to have the same technique. They still-hunt or soar, descending in steep glide on to prey which is often as heavy as the hawk itself.

Though I did not see the kill, I found *spilogaster* eating a full-grown dik-dik at Naivasha and at the same place I saw the same eagle drop steeply on to a guineafowl from his stance on a tree; so rapid was the attack that the guinea-fowl had no time to take wing. It has also been related to me that *spilogaster* will raid poultry, alighting near his prey and running rapidly after it.

Brown (*Eagles*, p. 95) saw Ayres's eagle snatching quail in long grass near Voi in Kenya, and make unsuccessful attacks on babblers.

In Central Asia Bonelli's eagle is trained to catch gazelle in conjunction with greyhounds, the bird attacking the animal's head, enabling the dogs to catch up and bind to. Bonelli's main technique is a lightning swoop on to the ground or into a tree. I have seen them crash into a thick evergreen tree and secure a green pigeon; and near Jedda I saw one swoop on to a small rodent, the latter just escaping into its hole. The hawk, so great was the impact, slid along the ground for several feet with outspread tail and wings in a cloud of sand, pulled himself together with a thoroughly disappointed look, and flew off lazily on to a rock hoping nobody had seen the failure. They readily take hares, their twists and turns as the hare jinks surpassing the agility of a greyhound, and they are much quicker and more agile than the more clumsy golden eagle. They have been known to kill a full-grown turkey and return the following day for another, and in Iraq they have been seen to take hoobara bustard and carry them off in flight. That grand old shikari, Donald of the Indian Police, told me he had seen a grey-lag goose taken from the ground.

The frequency with which I have seen Bonelli's eagle sitting in trees or on outstanding rocks and so seldom on the wing, leads me to believe that their normal technique is still-hunting. The angle of descent on to prey is about 45 degrees, wings partly flexed and tail half-fanned.

The booted eagle uses much the same technique as Bonelli's. When attacking poultry they have a complete disregard for man. Their usual technique is to sit unobtrusively in a thick-foliaged tree, whence they emerge at tremendous speed on to their victim without apparent check in speed on impact. A dove or pigeon stands little chance if feeding on the ground.

When I was having breakfast with Michael Nicoll on the island in the Giza Zoological Gardens, a booted eagle, which had been sitting unnoticed in a neighbouring tree, dashed across our view at a steep angle with wings half-furled and legs well to the fore. The speed was like lightning. He bumped into a palm-dove on the ground with terrific impact, no checking being apparent. He at once flew off with his victim. This episode is the more astonishing because one knows the alertness of doves on the ground and their ability to get away at lightning speed. I can only imagine that the dove was so taken by surprise that he crouched and was caught.

In Kenya I saw one dash into a tree in which a flock of guineafowl had taken refuge from a dog and, regardless of foliage and branches, seize a full-grown guineafowl and carry it off to another tree for the meal; they have also been known to take a dachshund puppy.

I can imagine no better killer for the enthusiastic falconer residing in bush or forest country, for they follow their quarry in and out of trees and seldom fail to kill. But I have never heard of a trained booted eagle.

In the Syrian desert I was taken out by an Arab falconer who had two trained jugger falcons. He flew them at three hoobara bustard; the hawk bound to one and then suddenly left it for no apparent reason, flying round in circles and screaming; then before we realised what was happening a Bonelli's eagle came down like a thunderbolt at a very steep angle, crashed into the bustard, stood there for a few seconds and, observing us approaching and shouting, flew off with the bird without difficulty. A hoobara weighs about the same as a Bonelli.

GOLDEN EAGLE
Aquila chrysaëtus

The golden eagle ranges throughout the Holarctic Region and south in Arabia to the tropics.

Golden eagles, and in fact all true eagles, kill by grasp and not by strike. Ground rodents appear to be the most popular food, but such oddities as porcupines, rattlesnakes, salmon, grasshoppers and skylarks have been found at eyries (Seton Gordon, *The Golden Eagle*, 1955).

There is no doubt that on occasions an eagle will take a living lamb, but that is no excuse for slaughtering every eagle; the crimes of a single delinquent teddy-boy is no excuse for locking up the whole human race. Seton Gordon (*op. cit.*) had only two authentic records of lamb-killing, and the only case I have come across was vitiated by the fact that the lamb had its eyes removed, which is not an eagle's work but that of crows or gulls. But so ingrained is this belief in lamb-killing in some parts of Scotland that I know of two crofters who, in order to prove their case, deliberately placed two dead lambs below an eyrie in order to convince the owner of an eagle's guilt. Perhaps in the United States, where sheep farming is more extensive than in Europe, the attraction of lambs as food may be greater than it is over here. Gordon (*op. cit.*) states that one hunter in Texas in eight years killed 8,300 eagles from an aeroplane! Knowing the American worship of high figures, I just do not believe it.

Golden eagles can carry a new-born lamb and a full-grown hare but do not always do so; the victim is often dismembered before carrying.

Sharp (*Journ. Wildlife Manag.*, XV, pp. 224-6) records that golden eagles occasionally killed young swan (*buccinator*) and found both common and Barrow's goldeneye easy to capture on the wing, but their stoops at mallard were less successful. They seemed unable to take duck off the water.

The golden eagle will make full use of his wings in knocking fawns and lambs off balance before grasping them; and they have been seen to send a hare sprawling by a blow with the wing.

They both soar in search of prey and will still-hunt. When soaring the pair often combine, though far apart, coming together when a likely prey is sighted.

Carnie (*Condor*, 1954, pp. 3-12) gives the food of seventeen pairs of eagles in California over a period of five years. 17 per cent of food was mammals, mostly rabbit and squirrel, 13 per cent birds, 6 per cent snakes and 4 per cent fish.

I have seen the golden eagle hunting on five occasions with varying success.

First: Braemore, Scotland, 8 September 1900. While we were deer-stalking an eagle appeared above us and flushed two coveys of ptarmigan (*Lagopus mutus*). The bird was flying low, skimming the steep slopes, and without doubt had in mind disturbing ptarmigan. The two coveys flew across a wide corrie, uniting as they went, and when less than half-way across we heard the swish of wings above us and saw a second eagle diving at the covey at an angle of about 45 degrees. The bird's wings were half-closed and he was travelling at terrific speed, fast overtaking the terrified covey, which was by now fully alarmed and doing a certain amount of zigzagging. Without checking, a victim was seized in mid-air and the eagle flew off in leisurely fashion, the ptarmigan dangling. The bird was seized by the talons. The first eagle was now seen hurrying off after his mate, and perhaps the whole hunt was staged. The ptarmigan were at least 1,000 feet above the bottom of the corrie at the moment of attack.

Second: Quetta, 27 March 1914. While I was out on Murdar Hill after chukar (*Alectoris graeca*) a covey was flushed on a steep slope. They dived down the hill, flattened out and turned off across a broad valley to another ridge. As I watched them there was a rush of wings above me and a golden eagle hurtled down on to them, gathering speed as he went, with wings half-closed, and descending at an angle of about 45 degrees. The eagle was among his victims in an instant, and though some of the covey attempted to scatter, a victim was seized in mid-air and the eagle flew off in leisurely fashion to devour his meal. In both this and the previous case the speed was attained by gravity alone, no wing-flapping being observed. The victim was taken by using one leg only, but was subsequently held by both legs. At the instant of striking the tail fanned out and the wings spread for flight.

Third: Kosseima (Sinai), 13 February 1928. A covey of coroneted sandgrouse (*Pterocles coronatus*) alighted on some bare desert about 200 yards from water and were slowly walking towards the drinking spot when a single golden eagle swooped down from the heavens and passed a few feet over them. The covey flattened out and froze, no doubt the eagle's intention. The eagle turned quickly and came to ground about twenty paces from them and at once commenced to scan the skies for his mate, who soon appeared with a rush, and again stooped at the covey. The eagle on the ground now commenced to walk slowly towards the covey, whilst his mate in the air repeated the stooping tactics over the covey, which had now flattened themselves out almost to obliteration. Then when the walking eagle, who was not more than six feet from the sandgrouse, was about to break into an amble, up rose the covey, with terrified 'guttas' and made off. The eagles looked stupid and made no attempt to follow. The pace with which those sandgrouse rose, gained height and vanished into the desert was incredible.

Fourth: East Ross-shire, 26 October 1930. During a hare drive on the high tops, with a heavy black snow-cloud blanketing the bare slopes, a blue hare came lolloping up the hill toward my butt. When he was within about eighty yards of me there was a rush of wings from behind and I saw an eagle bearing down towards him at terrific pace, with wings drawn in and feet slightly projecting. The hare saw him and dodged into a peat-hag, thus avoiding the first onslaught. The eagle made a lightning turn and followed the hare dodging among the hags. A second eagle now appeared from above, descending to ground-level at great speed and joining in the hunt. The ground favoured the hare, who, by zigzagging among the hags, did not seem to be experiencing much difficulty in evading his two pursuers, though both birds were never more than a few yards behind their victim and displaying remarkable quickness in turning, though flying but a foot or so above the ground with feet out, prepared to grab when a favourable moment occurred. The end was not witnessed, as snow and sleet commenced to fall and the scene was soon obscured in driving snow. If that hare failed to find cover in a cairn or hole he doubtless fell a victim to the two eagles, who were clearly out for blood.

Fifth : In late September 1944 I was at Scourie in Sutherland. The cloud ceiling was low and rain was driving in from the south-west. Suddenly I heard the call of geese and looking up I saw a skein of seven grey-lag flying towards the sea and about 500 feet up. They were calling loud and often because one of their number had lagged behind and could be seen about fifty yards behind the main body. As I watched, and not over 200 yards from me, a golden eagle planed down through the clouds towards the laggard goose who was now honking blue murder and performing all sorts of zigzag evasive action in the hope of averting disaster. The eagle came up behind the goose and slightly below it, turned on his back and seized the bird from below with a smack which I clearly heard (see plate 25 facing p. 112. The eagle must have got his talons well fixed in the goose for both fell in a tangled mass behind a rise and were lost to sight. I was too wet, tired and hungry to make any further investigation but have little doubt as to the end of that encounter. The main skein of geese, instead of bunching, as I had expected, scattered in every direction, registering their disapproval with loud honks. I was sorry for that lone goose.

Golden eagles are seldom successful after blue hares unless they come on them in soft snow or away from peat-hag country, the hare beating them by twists and turns in very broken country, where the eagle with his huge span and constant banking cannot flatten out low enough to seize his victim, his wing tips often scraping snow or peat, delaying speed and hindering quick turns. On one occasion on Ben Wyvis I witnessed an eagle stoop at a hare on open snow over the flat of the bottom of a steep corrie. The hare made for broken ground but was brought up against a solid wall of snow and when the eagle was gaining fast and about to seize him under most favourable con- ditions, the hare suddenly turned just before the snow bank was reached and the eagle crash-dived into the snow, unable to check his speed and without room to turn. There was a small avalanche of powdered snow as the bewildered eagle extricated himself and sat for a moment dazed, abandoning hare-hunting for that afternoon. After shaking himself and sitting for a moment in un- certainty, he resumed his majestic pose and sailed down the corrie.

I have seen a golden eagle playing with its victim in the air, rising to a considerable height with a ptarmigan, dropping it and then stooping to it, picking it up again and rising to drop it again.

All eagles will eat carrion, the golden eagle probably less than others, possibly because his wild habitats throughout his range are not littered with dead camels, donkeys and other beasts.

The golden eagle seems to me to prefer hunting in pairs, often with close co-operation; this is not a pronounced habit with other true eagles, except Verreaux's.

On Ben Wyvis I saw a large fox galloping over peat-hag with a rabbit in his mouth; with a swish of wings an eagle glided down towards the marauder, who dropped the rabbit and faced the eagle with ears back and bared teeth. I hoped for a good fight. The eagle checked when a few feet from the fox and made threatening little stoops at the animal, the fox facing the eagle and sometimes even jumping up and snapping at his tormentor. Finally the eagle settled not twenty yards from the fox and thus they remained facing each other for some ten minutes, when the fox, anxious to get on with his prey, picked up the rabbit and made off; but to his dismay he was soon followed by the eagle who stooped dangerously low at the fox; this was too much; the fox abandoned his rabbit and made off, brush down; the eagle picked up the pirated rabbit and flew off with his prize.

Gordon (*Field*, 7 March 1957, p. 339) quotes cases where a fox in Scotland held its brush aloft when faced by an eagle, and gives two cases where eagles have bound on to foxes and carried them up to over thirty feet before releasing them.

Miner (*Condor*, 1954, p. 223) describes how two eagles made an unsuccessful attack on a coyote in Colorado.

The killing grasp of a golden eagle is extremely powerful. At Mottisfont we had an adult eagle in a large cage. The gardener's cat ventured inside; the eagle contemplated the cat for about two minutes and then descended on it from its perch; the cat was too slow to realise the danger. The grasp with both feet, one on the head and neck and the other on the fore part of the body, killed the cat instantaneously—not a move or a miaow.

There are many reliable records of this eagle killing large mammals in both America and Europe—roe-deer, white-tailed deer, pronghorn antelope and sheep. On the other hand, others in many districts could find no evidence of sheep or lamb-killing.

PLATE 25

Golden Eagle and Goose

Lano (*Auk*, 1922, p. 258) records an attack by this eagle on a porcupine, the bird being covered with quills underneath and a number in the roof of the mouth.

Seton Gordon (*Hill Birds of Scotland*, 1915) records a desperate struggle between a fox and an eagle, the former catching hold of the eagle's breast and the eagle striking with its wings; eventually the eagle managed to become airborne with the fox still hanging on and gained a considerable height when the fox relinquished its hold and fell dead. A fox will weigh 16 lb.

The late Colonel Shoolbred had a female golden eagle mounted at Wyvis Lodge in East Ross; the bird had been killed by a hind protecting her young. The stalker told me he had watched the fight from close by; it had lasted for about fifteen minutes, the eagle constantly trying to get at the calf in thick heather and the hind standing up on her hind legs and striking the eagle with her forepaws. Eventually the eagle was struck in the neck and fell dead with a huge gash and dislocated vertebrae.

Without doubt the golden eagle exercises a selective influence on wild life. Sick or wounded animals are easier to kill than healthy ones. In Scotland and elsewhere many wounded hares and feathered game must be put out of their misery by eagles.

TAWNY AND STEPPE EAGLES
Aquila rapax and *nipalensis*

I believe these two eagles to be conspecific and therefore treat them together. They are mainly offal and carrion feeders, seldom killing for themselves unless it is a sick or wounded animal and then one much smaller than themselves. They will accompany shooting parties and come to the sound of guns. I have also seen them soaring with vultures. Near Aden I saw one sitting beside a curled-up hedgehog, uncertain of procedure, and another swoop down on a pack of sandgrouse, the latter easily evading disaster by taking flight.

In Somaliland I have seen as many as seventeen attracted by a sandgrouse-coming-to-water shoot, sitting around on tall acacia and at once pursuing a pricked or wounded bird. On one occasion a small Somali boy raced after a winged bird, closely followed by a large steppe eagle. They reached the sandgrouse almost simultaneously, the eagle buffeting the small boy with its wings and the boy hitting out at the eagle with a small stick; the eagle was too quick and snatched the bird almost from the boy's hand. On another occasion, at Erigavo in Somaliland, we had seven of these eagles sitting round our camp waiting for carcases of skinned birds which were constantly being thrown out, and these they would retrieve. When food was scarce we saw them soaring with vultures, taking full advantage of the latter's locating and descending on to carrion. These eagles will sometimes drive vultures off carrion if their numbers exceed those of the vultures.

In Morocco I found a solitary eagle sitting low down in a tree, bobbing its head and looking intently at the ground. Working my way cautiously behind a cactus hedge I found the object of his interest—a mangy jackal feeding on some carrion. At that moment some bulbuls sounded the alarm note and off slunk the jackal, but the eagle paid no attention to a warning from small birds; he at once flopped down on to the half-finished meal but suddenly became alarmed and resumed his seat in the tree; I thought the jackal was returning—and so, I suspect, did the eagle. But instead of the jackal a mongoose with three babies appeared. The eagle's reaction was immediate; he did not flop down this time but dived like a thunderbolt on to the mongoose family, crushing the life out of the mother; the babies fled. It was a tragedy which impressed me much at the time. The survival of the fittest, might is right, the suddenness of death, piracy, robbery and murder—the laws of the jungle.

In Egypt I came across a large female tawny eagle feeding on a piece of carrion. A large mongoose approached and the eagle backed away from its food, the mongoose with arched back and tail upright standing about six feet away; the eagle and mongoose stood facing each other; if the eagle showed signs of resuming his meal the mongoose would threaten with little jumps; if the mongoose attempted to take a bite the eagle would threaten with a jump and a flap or two; so the game went on, neither daring to eat, until a couple of hooded crows settled the question and proceeded to feed on the disputed morsel, eagle and mongoose watching at a respectful distance.

K. Eates (*epist.*, Oct. 1957) records an encounter between a tawny eagle (*Aquila rapax*) and three hoobara bustard (*Chlamydotis*). A single eagle was on the ground facing three bustard about fifteen feet away, two on one side of him and one on the other side. The eagle, panting from exhaustion after probably a long pursuit, suddenly ran at the single bustard who crossed toward the other two, who themselves crossed to where the single one had been, thus confusing the eagle; this happened several times, the bustard crossing in front of the eagle thus confusing him. The eagle was thoroughly confused and exhausted, with drooping wings, but on spotting Eates flew off. Eates also records other cases of criss-cross tactics by bustard which are clearly aimed at confusing eagles. Eates adds: 'We know that this bustard squirts the viscid fluid contents of its lower gut at a close-pursuing hawk. Is, then, the confusing criss-cross manoeuvre on the ground another form of defence characteristic of the species and does the hoobara know that by adopting these tactics it confuses the eagle? Apparently the avian ability to see more ways than the direct front at one time is responsible to some extent for the confusion caused, but is the hoobara aware of this?'

For a somewhat similar case of anti-eagle tactics by bustard, see under Imperial Eagle.

IMPERIAL EAGLE
Aquila heliacus

I have seen many imperial eagles in Iraq but never in pursuit of prey, though I shot a specimen with a crop full of chukar near Baghdad.

Hume, who boasted that he had shot over a hundred of this magnificent bird (seven in one morning), calls it a 'great hulking kite.' They have been known to kill a half-grown peacock in India and to capture partridges and duck on the wing.

When on the plains east of Mosul in Iraq, I came across this eagle sitting about thirty feet from five hoobara, the eagle with slightly drooping wings and the bustard very active, running hither and thither, sometimes concentrating and sometimes each running quickly for a short distance and then coming back. The eagle suddenly made a quick run at them but the bustard separated at great speed, two of them completing a circle round the eagle. This clearly confused the eagle who looked in all directions watching the scattered bustard, who finally concentrated again not twenty paces from the eagle. The eagle then with half-flexed wings made a running dash at the bustard who rose in flight against the wind and towards the eagle who crouched and allowed the bustard to pass over his head without any effort to rise and seize one. The eagle never attempted to follow them and finally went off in an opposite direction completely discomfited.

This evidenced the cowardly nature of the imperial eagle. Any of the large falcons, the golden eagle, Bonelli's or booted eagle would not have hesitated one moment if he had wanted one of those bustard but would have

Imperial eagle in flight

crashed into one and bound to. The bustard would have concentrated at his attack and might have pecked the eagle off.

The Spanish race (*adalberti*) has much the same habits, preferring wounded or sick prey and not showing either pluck or enterprise when hunting. During duck shooting in the Marismas of southern Spain, one or two would come to the sound of the guns and wait on for wounded birds ; but when a goose landed with a broken wing, the eagle landed near it without any attempt to seize it. The goose stood its ground facing the eagle and, though the latter was almost twice the size of the goose, the eagle had not sufficient courage—or appetite—to attack a victim which might retaliate. We captured the goose, brought it to England where it lived for two years and then suddenly discovered that it could fly and off it went.

On another occasion in the Marismas, when chasing the wild camels splashing through water and bog, a pair of these magnificent birds followed us watching for disturbed creatures and were rewarded by a hare which they chased and caught after many twists and turns.

PLATE 26

Verreaux's Eagle and piglet

VERREAUX'S EAGLE (Dassievanger)
Aquila verreauxi

Verreaux's eagle is one of the finest of his kind both in looks, flight and habit; he ignores carrion and is fearless in pursuit of food. He ranges in Africa from Cape Province to Abyssinia and Somaliland.

He probably pairs for life and more than one person has recorded the regular beats and timings when hunting. In Nandi (Kenya), where I lived for a year, I could almost set my watch by the time one of them would pass my house.

Hyrax is the staple diet but animals as large as baboon and leopard have been attacked. They have been known to knock klipspringer and small antelope with their wings when caught on steep slopes.

Not far from my house in Nandi was a huge boulder commanding a magnificent view of the surrounding country. It was a feeding-stance and observatory for a pair of Verreaux's eagles, its base being strewn with the remains of small cats, hyrax and small antelope. On one occasion when I was watching a Verreaux on the rock a small sounder of wart-hog passed below, the old sow entering an old ant-bear hole while the very small squealers played outside. The eagle took note of the porkers, intently watching them and bowing her head towards them, contemplating an attack. She suddenly launched herself towards the unsuspecting family of baby pig and, without apparently checking speed, bumped right on top of one of them; the remainder scuttled for the ant-bear hole, creating a traffic block at the entrance.

The victim must have been killed at once for there was no apparent struggle. After waiting about a minute, and not once looking at her victim but gazing around for possible interference, she flew off with her meal to her favourite boulder where she was joined by her mate. After eating their fill, the pair of eagles flew off and what remained of the carcase rolled down off the boulder. The talons had pierced the spine at two points in the neck, the throat was badly lacerated and the arteries severed.

In 1909 I met a farmer at Harrismith in the Transvaal who had a pair of Verreaux's resident on his estate. He told me they lived almost entirely on hyrax, an occasional young rhebok and many young baboons; they never raided his poultry or lambs, and in return for keeping the baboon in check he never molested the eagles. They had never to his knowledge come to carrion.

This same farmer told me the technique employed by these eagles when attacking baboon; he had seen two successful attacks and many failures, the latter occurring when the pack of baboon had a little warning and were able to get near their young and protect them. Both successful attacks resulted in quite babies being snatched when a little distance from their mothers. The eagle swooped down and snatched without landing, the baby being carried off all in one movement amid intense jabbering.

A few years ago a Verreaux's eagle took a pekinese dog in the Matopos in Rhodesia. The little dog had strayed and was never seen again.

THE SPOTTED EAGLES
Aquila clanga and *pomarina*

I have only once seen *A. clanga*—in Estonia, when a single bird was flushed from a dead hare. They are largely carrion-eaters and prey on other animals much smaller than themselves.

The lesser spotted eagle (*pomarina*) and the larger (*clanga*) are both un-enterprising and cowardly. I have never seen either attack a healthy victim. In the Deccan I shot an Alpine swift which fell some two hundred yards from me. With a rush, down came a lesser spotted eagle, seized my swift and made off with it.

At Bharatpur in Rajputana, where many will sit about in trees around the famous duck-shooting ground, they are quick to pick up wounded birds. On one occasion a wounded duck fell on dry land; an eagle went after it but the duck could flutter along at a good pace; the eagle ran after it for about fifty yards, at quite a good pace, eventually securing it. This small eagle is attracted to the sound of guns, knowing it means wounded birds, and at many duck shoots and sandgrouse shoots I have seen as many as a dozen birds waiting on for wounded birds.

BLACK EAGLE
Ictinaëtus malayensis

In Sikkim a black eagle was seen to swoop into a tea plantation at a steep angle with wings half-furled and legs to the fore. He soon flew off with a

PLATE 27

AQUILA POMARINA
Lesser spotted Eagle ♂
from life

Lesser-spotted Eagle

snake dangling from his talons. On another occasion this eagle was seen to drop from a tree on to the ground close by (obviously 'still' hunting) and a cuckoo-dove arose from the spot, so presumably the attack was unsuccessful.

WHITE-TAILED SEA-EAGLE
Haliaëtus albicilla

Resident in the Palaearctic Region south to the Mediterranean and formerly in Egypt.

A clumsy, heavily built eagle, preying mainly on sick or wounded animals, carrion and fish. Its habits exercise a selective influence on life. It has been known to take small dogs, lambs, domestic poultry, hares and any kind of large bird which is wounded or sick or for some reason is not up to standard. A conspicuous characteristic when hunting is the throwing forward of the legs with talons extended ready to seize, long before contact with prey is expected. Every other large eagle I have seen hunting keeps its legs close in until the moment for seizing occurs.

I have seen this eagle hunting in Greenland, Norway, the Baltic and in Hungary. In the latter country a flapping eagle over a grassy plain suddenly turned aside to where a great bustard was standing motionless. When it was about a hundred yards from the bustard, the latter took flight and the eagle at once abandoned the hunt. At some preserved fish ponds near by, two of these eagles appeared one afternoon; they had no difficulty in catching the many hand-fed carp which swam lazily near the surface. In three cases the fish was snatched without wetting the eagle. But there are cases on record of the eagle splashing right into the water.

Mauersberger (epist., 1958) records this sea-eagle in the Baltic being violently mobbed by herring gulls, one of which ventured too close ; ' With a sudden and elegant twist the eagle grasped the gull in flight and flew off to a post where it plucked its victim '.

Fischer (Beitr. Vogelk., 1958, p. 314) records this eagle swimming to shore with a victim.

An eagle will often swoop down on geese and duck on the water, but is seldom successful in snatching a victim. The aim of the eagle is, I believe, to detect a lame or sick bird. Even swans have been threatened in this way but if they react as healthy birds they are not molested.

If duck or geese fly away when threatened the eagle passes on, but if the duck dives, the eagle will then take interest and endeavour to snatch when the victim surfaces. This technique, even with healthy duck, can be successful, for if the eagle persists the victim tires and is eventually snatched exhausted from the surface. The late J. G. Millais recounted to me how he had seen a pair of eagles tire out a great northern diver off the Lofoten Islands and eventually secure it. He painted the picture here reproduced which is a close copy of a similar incident painted by Bruno Liljefors.

Absorbing or emulating another man's art or style or philosophy and presenting it in slightly different form has been done throughout the ages and is still done. There is nothing vicious about it. Nearly all creative artists have done it, even though unconsciously. After all, every description of art, once published, is public property, to be admired, copied and absorbed by all. Millais, far from denying Liljefors's influence on his work, gloried in it, seeing no harm in it and, to my mind, deserving no censure. I cannot join those who think ill of Johnny Millais for emulating the art of others. Originality of the artist is originality of treatment, not of the subject, and I consider that in some ways Millais's copies of Liljefors's work are in fact better than Liljefors's original.

Rudebeck (*Oikos*, 1951, p. 219) records a heron being captured in flight and an injured bean goose, incapable of flight, warding off an attack by beating its wings against the eagle. He also records several attacks on flying or rising geese without success. This eagle is also an inveterate pirate, forcing osprey, gulls and snowy owls to abandon their food.

Gavin Maxwell (*A Reed shaken by the Wind*, 1957, p. 76) gives a vivid account of an attack on coot by sea-eagles in the Euphrates marshes:

Far out in the middle of the lake lay a long solid line, perhaps a mile of it, and dark as charcoal. As I looked at this my eye was caught by something above it, something hurtling down like a diving aircraft, and then another and another. A line of white foam suddenly edged the dark strip that looked like land, and a muttering roar like the undertow of a wave came to us across the mile of still water. The dark line was formed of coot, many, many thousands of them, bunched together under the repeated attacks of five eagles. The eagles could not strike while the coot remained on the water, and again and again they hurtled downward, trying to panic the great throng into taking wing. Under each attack the whole mass spread

PLATE 28

White-tailed Sea Eagles and Diver

their wings and scuttered forward for a few yards, driving a frothing wave before them, and as the eagle pulled out of his dive and began to climb again the coot bunched tightly together so that one could not have dropped a pin between them.

In Scotland, where they were abundant a hundred years ago, sea-eagles would take up their residence near colonies of sea birds but would also hunt inland where their depredations on sheep have been much exaggerated. But as usual, the sheep farmer, the gamekeeper and the egg-collector slowly exterminated them. Dresser (*B. Europe*, v, p. 555) records that a keeper in Skye shot fifty-seven on a single estate and another in West Ross-shire shot fifty-two in twelve years, besides taking numbers of both eggs and young. Such revolting slaughter is unforgivable, depriving us for all time of seeing this magnificent bird in its natural surroundings.

PALLAS'S SEA-EAGLE
Haliaëtus leucoryphus

I have seen Pallas's sea-eagle snatching fish on the Wular Lake in Kashmir and on the Indus River in Ladak. But I suspect that its main food is other game, for of many broods of the bar-headed goose on Shushal Lake in Ladak, but one youngster remained in July; the eagles had their nest just above the lake and during the few days I stayed there had taken one adult goose and several ruddy sheld-duck. In Kashmir, where they breed in the magnificent plane trees, I had a nest watched for three days, during which period fish were brought to the single young bird on one occasion and birds on seven occasions; from the remains below the nest it seemed that the majority of the victims were the little bittern which breeds in large numbers on the lake round Srinagar. I have also seen this eagle hunting reed-beds like a huge harrier near Lucknow, when he was successful in retrieving a cotton teal I had wounded before I could reach it. The flight is particularly buoyant and active when hunting, though sluggish and almost clumsy when not hunting.

The larger sea-eagles will sometimes get fast into a fish which is too heavy for them. On the Indus near Skardu I saw a Pallas's sea-eagle catch a large fish; in attempting to lift it he was dragged almost to complete submersion before he had to abandon his catch after a struggle lasting several minutes.

Near Quetta this eagle used to turn up occasionally at Khushdil Khan, a large sheet of water covered with waterfowl of all descriptions in winter, including geese. In January 1914 I saw one hunting geese, both grey-lag and bar-fronted. He would fly low over them, slowly driving them into shallow water, the geese making clumsy dives as he approached; but in shallow water the goose had difficulty in achieving total submersion, its legs and tail being exposed; that was the eagle's opportunity and on two occasions it caught bar-headed in that manner, seizing them by the stomach and carrying them off to land, the goose struggling and honking. On landing the eagle would transfer his grip to the head and neck, killing the goose instantaneously.

AMERICAN BALD EAGLE
Haliaëtus leucocephalus

This eagle became the national emblem of the United States in 1782 and has been systematically persecuted ever since. In Alaska 16·9 per cent of its food was salmon (Imler and Kalmbach, *Fish and Wild Life Service*, 1955). About 19 per cent was birds. Two-thirds of its food was fish.

I have seen them on the Hudson River near New York, when quite small fish were snatched from the surface and carried to the bank; unlike ospreys, they carry fish anyhow.

It has been related to me how this eagle was seen to get fast into a large salmon in the sea off British Columbia, and being unable either to lift the salmon or to disengage its talons, was left literally spreadeagled and exhausted on the surface, soaked through but still fast in his fish. Both bird and fish were eventually caught by a boy who was salmon-fishing in the neighbourhood.

Maynard (*Birds of Eastern N. America*, 1896) records an attack on young pigs, and Oberholser (*U.S. Biol. Surv. Bull.*, xvii, 1906) gives instances of attacks on mule deer, reindeer and foxes; they will often catch duck on the wing by stooping or level flight.

Rand (*Bull. U.S. Nat. Mus.*, 1937, p. 328) recounts this eagle attacking a raft of coot, closely huddled together and using splashing tactics, the eagle constantly attacking until a few coot became separated from the raft and fell easy victims; on one occasion a coot evaded the eagle by diving, but the eagle dived after his victim, remaining 'some seconds under water,' finally appearing with the bird in its talons but so exhausted that he could scarcely fly.

PLATE 29

Steller's Sea Eagle

Brewster (*Bull. Nuttall Orn. Club*, 1880, p. 57) records an eagle attacking wild geese, suddenly sweeping beneath the victim, turning over and seizing the goose by the breast. If they fall in water the eagle 'literally tows its prize along the surface until the shore is reached; in this way one has been known to drag a large goose for nearly a mile.'

Rand (*op. cit.*, p. 329) also records this eagle diving after his prey but 'was unable to raise it from the water, and after struggling awhile he lay with wings extended and apparently exhausted. After resting a minute or two he again raised himself out of the water and I saw he had some large black object in the grasp of one of his talons, which he succeeded in towing along the top of the water toward the shore a short distance and then letting go his hold. He was then joined by two other eagles and by taking turns they soon succeeded in getting it to the shore. Investigation proved it to be a large Florida cormorant, on which they were about to regale themselves.'

Fish is the main food supply, either direct catching, or scavenging on the shore or robbing ospreys; in the latter case the osprey usually drops the fish before contact but sometimes the eagle comes up from below, turns on its back in the air and literally seizes the fish from the osprey's grasp. They have been known to watch holes in the ice for fish which surface there and they have been seen to catch a flying fish in flight. They will also compel vultures to disgorge, and kill them if the vulture is too slow or unable to disgorge.

Wilson (*American Ornithology*, 1832) records a case of a human baby being attacked and a fragment of its frock being torn off.

STELLER'S SEA-EAGLE   KOREAN SEA-EAGLE
Haliaëtus pelagicus   *Haliaëtus niger*

When my brother Dan and I were boys we bought two immature sea-eagles in the London Docks, both reputed to be Steller's. On reaching adult plumage the larger turned out to be Steller's and the smaller the rare Korean sea-eagle. George Lodge, who frequently stayed with us at Mottisfont, painted their portraits (see also plate 32 facing p. 135).

While Steller's would eat any sort of meat given him and preferred rabbit and giblets to fish, the Korean eagle would eat little but fish, sometimes refusing other meat even when hungry.

I can find nothing in literature about their mode of hunting or food preferences, though it may be hidden away in a mass of Russian literature which I cannot translate.

AFRICAN FISH EAGLE
Haliaëtus vocifer

Ranges almost throughout Africa south of the Sahara.

This eagle has been observed at work in many parts of Africa, and when my brother and I were boys in Hampshire we had a fine specimen, full-winged and perfectly free, about which I write later.

When hunting, this eagle does not dive like the osprey but snatches from the surface or just below the surface and the fish is carried for consumption to some tree or small eminence; unlike the osprey, the fish is carried as caught and not carried head to the front. On Lake Nyasa I have seen them take the small cormorant and eat a small teal. They will take wounded or sick duck and have been recorded by Brown (*Eagles*, p. 125) as taking the lesser flamingo on Lake Hannington. In *Ostrich* (1957, p. 9) is a recorded case from South Africa of this eagle raiding a heronry consisting mainly of cattle egrets (*Bubulcus*).

Two characteristics of this eagle stand out, the one charming and the other most reprehensible—his wild call and his piratical habit. His call with head thrown back is the voice of Africa and is almost always uttered when stationary. Once only, on the Victoria Nyanza, did I hear an attempt at his characteristic call when on the wing and on the way to pick up a dead pygmy cormorant which I had shot; the head was only partially thrown back.

His piratical habit is directed mainly against the osprey but also against heron, pelican and kites. Bannerman (*Birds of West Africa*, I, p. 63) records a case of this eagle stooping at a goliath heron and becoming impaled on the heron's beak. On the Victoria Nyanza, where the osprey is common, he will deliberately wait on, though he is an expert fisherman himself, and so soon as he sees an osprey catch a fish he chases the bird, who screams loudly but in the end has to drop his fish, which is recovered in the air before it reaches water. When there are no osprey he fishes for himself, snatching from the surface and seldom touching the water with his body.

PLATE 30

Griffon Vulture

On Lake Nyasa and on the Zambesi, in addition to fish, they will take the small cormorant and duck, and I once saw an unsuccessful attack on guineafowl.

On the Victoria Nyanza they are often seen in close proximity to the mixed breeding colonies of darters, cormorants, ibises, etc., sometimes sitting aloft right in the colony. But I have never seen them being mobbed, nor have I seen them interfere with nesting birds.

Pitman records it raiding a heronry (*Ardea melanocephala*) in Uganda, wrecking the nests, smashing the eggs and driving away the herons. Some 150 eggs were destroyed. The reason was not apparent but perhaps the eagles required the heronry for their own nest. Pitman adds: 'It is well known that this eagle and the goliath heron (*Ardea goliath*) are sworn enemies and the former rarely loses the opportunity of attacking or mobbing the latter.'

On Lake Albert there are at least six cases where this eagle has become entangled in plug-baits on which they have swooped.

Now about the specimen we had in Hampshire when we were boys. She was purchased for £10 from Jamrach's in the London Docks. She became perfectly tame and easily handled. She was given her liberty and remained at large for several years, being known as Lobengula. She would fish in the Test, always bringing her catch to a favourite chimney-pot on the old Abbey. To reach her fishing ground on the Test she had to run the gauntlet of two rookeries and a heronry, and these three communities would turn out in force to mob her; she disdained the rooks but took the herons seriously, turning over on her back if one came too close. During the mayfly season we had to shut her up as on one occasion she snatched a hooked fish from my father's rod, breaking the line. But trout were not her main prey; almost always roach, dace or perch, never a pike or eel.

Her wild call as she sat on her chimney-pot was a joy to hear; and whenever I heard it in Africa, I was reminded of my old home and Lobengula.

TRUE VULTURES

In 1905 when the late Abel Chapman visited Kenya, he and I shot a hartebeeste near Nairobi at a time when both game and vultures were abundant. Said

Abel, 'Let's lie on our backs and watch the vultures and see how long they take to descend.' So we did, lying concealed but a few feet from the dead hartebeeste, spying the heavens with binoculars. With the naked eye we saw nothing in the sky, but with glasses we soon picked up a few specks. Nothing happened for twenty minutes. So we turned the hartebeeste over on his back and cut open his stomach, returning to concealment. There was a good expanse of crimson blood and guts on the hartebeeste. Within five minutes we saw a vulture with half-flexed wings descending at an angle towards us; then, watching the heavens, we saw others like small specks, coming down at great speed until the sky seemed alive with descending birds, each attracted by the other and coming down from all directions. We lay perfectly still on our backs whilst the huge birds settled on the grass near us but none approaching the carcase; then a single bird commenced to walk slowly towards the carcase, then another and another whilst we remained motionless on our backs; then Abel could stand it no longer and jumped up with a yell, and some thirty great birds, thoroughly scared and deceived, flopped off at high speed.

Both Abel and I thought that the vultures had not recognised the hartebeeste as potential food until we cut him open and exposed blood and flesh. Red is the most conspicuous of all colours and perhaps what vultures look for is red colour. I have previously noted that no vultures have come to food until blood or flesh is exposed and I know of many cases where carcases of animals have remained untouched by vultures until either jackal or hyaena have opened them up.

Abel Chapman in *Wild Spain* gives a vivid description of griffons in Spain over half a century ago:

Presently there appeared far overhead, some half dozen griffon vultures wheeling in immense circles, the huge birds dwarfed by the altitude to mere specks. Then another stratum, still higher, was detected, and afterwards a keen eye distinguished a third, and then a fourth, beyond the average range of human vision. How many more tiers of soaring vultures might then occupy the regions of unseen space beyond, cannot be told; but the incident serves to illustrate the system on which Nature's great scavengers patrol the land. The lower strata we estimated at 800 to 1,000 yards altitude, and these only, it is probable, are on active service, the upper tiers merely standing by, ready to profit by the discoveries of all the working parties that may be in sight beneath them; for at the enormous elevations of the uppermost birds, it is impossible to suppose that even a vulture's eye could detect so small an object as, say, a dead goat on the earth.

TRUE VULTURES

Gyps fulvus, himalayensis, rüppelli and *indicus*

I have seen all these vultures soaring and at food and cannot see any difference in habit.

Food is obtained by sight from great heights and by watching other vultures descending, which draws others from immense distances until every vulture for perhaps fifty miles and over is concentrated to food. With binoculars I have seen vultures at over 6,000 feet above ground level when they are invisible to the naked eye. A large vulture is barely visible to the naked eye at 6,000 feet. Brown (*Eagles*, p. 167) claims that he identified a spotted eagle seven or eight miles distant—that is about 37,000 feet. A large aeroplane is invisible without binoculars at 37,000 feet.

Possibly the lower-level vultures soaring are the ones which first view food and the higher-level birds watch the lower-level birds.

On the Athi Plains of Kenya I came across a jackal lying on its back watching the skies, turning his head in all directions as though watching something in the skies. Quite suddenly he jumped to his feet and scampered off, continually looking up into the skies, and on following his gaze I saw vultures descending from all directions on to a carcase which proved to be a dead wildebeeste. The vultures got there first but were soon scattered by the jackal and had to sit around while he had his meal.

Frank Chapman (*My Tropical Air Castle*, 1929) experimented with the turkey-buzzard at Barro Colorado Island and thought they had a highly developed sense of smell. Other experiments with vultures and eagles draw an opposite conclusion with which I agree. I believe all hawks to be devoid of any sense of smell. I believe the source of error to lie in the fact that heaps of carrion concealed in bush or under any other cover will attract insects and small mammals, and these are seen by vultures ever on the look-out for movement of other carrion eaters.

The height at which vultures soar would preclude smell reaching them; also experiments with captive Raptores reduced to hunger show that they will not detect well-hidden putrefied meat.

Vultures will not begin feeding unless they are quite sure the corpse is dead; but they have been known to tackle tortoises.

When feeding, these vultures utter a low almost inaudible grunt. An

127

undamaged carcase is first opened at the anal aperture, nose, eyes and tongue; or if there is a wound it is enlarged, and the intestines exposed.

Birds will feed until gorged and sometimes unable to fly any distance. In Africa and Arabia where large carcases are being devoured, it is no uncommon sight to see a vulture right inside and hidden from view. In Somaliland I came across a griffon inside a camel; he could neither turn to come out nor could he back out; I pulled him out by his short tail.

Dresser (*B. Europe*, v, p. 378) records a score of griffon engaged in turning over a dead horse, one side of which they had already reduced to a skeleton.

The griffon must wander in search of food over southern Europe more frequently than is generally supposed. During the Franco-Prussian War of 1870–1 large numbers were attracted by dead horses; and the late Capt. Sanderson, a Crimean veteran, told me in 1904 that hundreds collected on the field of Balaclava after the charge of the Light Brigade and special squads were detailed to shoot them, as wounded men were by no means safe from their attentions.

CINEREOUS VULTURE
Aegypius monachus

Usually solitary; the most I have ever seen together was at Aden when five were in the air at one time. Both the griffon and Rüppell's vultures make way for them at food; other observers have noted them feeding amicably with the griffon. I have seen blood stream from a griffon's neck because he presumed to share a dead camel. I watched two trying to tackle a dead mule in the Balearic Islands; one effected an entrance via the anal cavity; the other, after removing the eyes, made an entry into the stomach after about five minutes' tearing.

EGYPTIAN VULTURE
Neophron percnopterus

One of the foulest scavengers, eating putrid offal which other vultures will not touch, even extending its beastliness to human and other excrement. On this account it has deserved the Anglo-Indian name 'shawk,' an abbreviation for something worse.

A great coward, avoiding a rat if it shows the slightest sign of life. I once tied a string to a sausage and threw it out to where one of these vultures was sitting. After a long inspection the bird alighted within a foot of the bait. I then gave a slight jerk to the string, moving the sausage an inch or two. The bird took immediate fright and would not again approach the sausage.

They drink a great deal and are fond of washing, sitting down in a few inches of water and emerging drenched; then walking to a hot rock to dry and preen. One seldom comes across this vulture with dirty plumage.

When soaring for food they reach great heights—mere specks in the sky. During the First World War in Sinai on more than one occasion anti-aircraft fire was directed on them at 5,000 feet, supposing them to be German aircraft.

They will congregate to locust swarms, devouring the insects in the air without removing wings.

Chapman (*Wild Spain*, p. 206) records them dropping bones on rock, as does the lammergeier (q.v.).

PALM-NUT VULTURE
Gypohierax angolensis

So far as I know this is the only Accipitrine which supplements a fish diet with a regular vegetable diet. Their distribution in Africa almost exactly coincides with that of the palms *Elaeis* and *Raphia*. Thomson and Moreau (*Ibis*, 1957, p. 608) summarise the food habits of this hawk. The fruits of *Elaeis* and *Raphia* are sometimes eaten entire; they also catch fish by snatch and will come down to dead fish; they also eat freshwater crabs, locusts and the large land snail *Achatina*.

Moreau (*op. cit.*, p. 612) has seen the African duck (*Anas sparsa*) strike and drive away this vulture from its territory.

LAMMERGEIER OR LAMMERVANGER
Gypaëtus barbatus

The lammergeier combines extreme grace in flight, an almost regal appearance in his natural surroundings with a cowardice out of all proportion to his size and magnificence. He is a bird of unashamed cowardice, ready to take advantage of any animal in distress, incapable of defending himself against creatures half his own size and frightened at the wink of an eyelid. And yet this bird of despicable character is one of the finest exponents of flight and aerial grace in the kingdom of birds. His poise, his long pointed wings, his torpedo body and his long wedge-shaped tail contribute to give him a greater majesty than any of the true eagles. The bateleur eagle is perhaps a more perfect airman, a ballet dancer or clown among birds, but his uncouth tail-less figure makes him almost ridiculous. There is nothing ridiculous about a lammergeier; he is sinister, magnificent and dignified. Seen at close quarters I know no bird so impressive.

I have lived in close contact with lammergeier in many parts of the world —Himalayas, Tibet, Afghanistan, Syria and Palestine, Sinai and Egypt, on Mount Kenya and in the Pyrenees and the Spanish mountains. He is to my mind the finest of the Raptores whether in flight or at rest; but his usual hunting technique is not so satisfactory. At times he can be bold and enterprising but in the vast majority of cases he is cowardly and craven. There have been many accounts of this huge bird knocking chamois and goats off cliffs, and then descending to feed on the mutilated corpse. The nearest approach to this technique came to my notice one evening in the hills north of Chakrata in the Himalayas. I had stalked and shot a gooral on a steep slope. The animal collapsed, apparently dead. I was considering my best approach to recover my game when an adult lammergeier came sweeping along the hill-face and deliberately struck my gooral with the tip of a wing. The gooral was not quite dead but the lammergeier turned at once and again struck the gooral, making it roll down the slope where it fetched up on a ledge. The lammergeier followed it down with amazing rapidity and no doubt would have attacked it again if I had not intervened.

Wolfe's famous picture of a lammergeier attacking a chamois with young may or may not be founded on fact. General Sir Ian Hamilton (*Listening for the Drums*, p. 111) records how he was attacked by a lammergeier when crossing a moving scree. When he was half-way across and in difficulties 'there was a tremendous swish in the air and my hat was sent spinning off my head down the precipice whilst I received a blow which all but made me follow it. I was being attacked by a lammergeier which was making circles round me.' The bird was eventually driven off by Sir Ian's shikari firing off a rifle. Sir Ian told me later that the blow was delivered by the talons.

There is also a record in Sir Alfred Pease's book (*Half a Century of Sport*, p. 166) where the author describes how he was attacked 'by a pair of great black eagles,' which made several circles high above his head and then swooped down at a lightning swish to within a foot or two of his head. He continues: 'I then stood up and waved my rifle but they repeated their attack . . . having a good look at me from six feet, swinging round me and then sheered off to the white precipices above me.'

I had a most unpleasant experience with a lammergeier in Baluchistan near Quetta. I was crossing a moving scree when it commenced to crawl; I travelled down the slope, eventually fetching up against a juniper stump to which I clung with boulders tearing downhill all round me. In this position a lammergeier came so close to me that I could see his red eye; three times he passed me within a few feet, aware that I was in difficulties, but after I threw rocks at him he made off.

A circumstantial account of a lammergeier taking a small girl is related in Dresser (*B. Europe*, v, p. 410). It happened in the Bernese Oberland in 1763. The father had taken his little girl aged three and put her to sleep in a field. When he returned she was gone. Later on a child's scream was heard, a friend ran to the sound, disturbed a lammergeier and rescued the child uninjured except for wounds in the arm and hand. The child was rechristened Lammergeier-Anni.

I have searched literature in vain for a reliable case of a lammergeier seizing and killing even a rat or venturing to tackle even a wounded animal. He will, I am convinced, knock his prey off cliffs and mountain slopes in the hope that it may fall to death. I believe the lammergeier is incapable of seizing prey and killing it. The legs are powerful but the talons are blunt; also, when a lammergeier sights food he does not swoop down to it but circles round and eventually lands on the ground near by, then walks cautiously towards it, very cautiously, eyeing it from all directions and then, having satisfied himself that the food is really dead, he will commence to feed.

The nearest approach to seizing a living animal occurred in Quetta in 1913: the lammergeier was a barrack-room scavenger alongside the kite, recovering bones and offal thrown out from cook-houses and the men's plates; a ten-inch puppy was floundering about close to the men having their dinners when a lammergeier landed alongside it, looked at it, jumped on it and carried it off; the puppy yelped, the men shouted and the puppy was dropped.

For centuries it has been a common belief that lammergeiers carry bones to a considerable height and drop them for the purpose of breaking them. That they do carry bones to a great height and drop them has been observed by many, but is it done to break them? The origin of this belief appears to have been the dropping of a tortoise on the bald head of Aeschylus, the bird mistaking it for a stone. Osbert Salvin, quoted by Dresser in *Birds of Europe*, says that the main food of the lammergeier in the Atlas Mountains is the tortoise, which is carried to some height and then let fall to break the shell.

Do lammergeiers have a regular place or slab of rock on which they drop bones in the hope of splintering them so that the marrow can be extracted? North, quoting Moreau (*Ibis*, 1948, p. 140), describes such a place on a rocky ridge north-west of Mount Kenya; the slab of rock was about forty yards square, was littered with bones and fragments of bones—'about a dozen pails full'—but there was only one splash to denote that a large bird had been there. No lammergeier was seen. This ossuary may have been that of porcupines, though I have never seen one on such a large scale, or, of course, it may have been a lammergeier's bone-dropping place; I do not regard it as proven.

Verner (*My Life among the Wild Birds of Spain*, 1909) saw several cases of bone-dropping by lammergeier and the habit was well known to the locals; but no evidence was found of a regular ossuary nor was there any proof that bones were dropped for cracking. Surely if the lammergeier had regular ossuaries these would be known in the Himalayas and Baluchistan where the bird is common, and in Spain where it used to be common?

Fleming (*Bomb. N.H. Soc. Journ.*, 1955, p. 933) gives several cases where this habit has been observed in the Himalayas and I have frequently seen the lammergeier fly up with bones and drop them, sometimes on rocks and sometimes on soft earth. When a lammergeier carries a bone up in his claws he is constantly fumbling with it, pecking at it with his beak and moving its position; this often leads to the bone being dropped; sometimes, not always, the bird will descend and repeat the process. The femur of an ox will crack if carried to a hundred feet and dropped on solid stone, but if dropped on shale, rubble or earth it does not crack. I carried out this experiment at Quetta.

PLATE 31

Lammergeier (from a tapestry by the Author)

In Afghanistan I saw a lammergeier pick up a small tortoise about six inches long, fly up with it and drop it at random; it fell on soft ground though there was ample rock in the vicinity; the process was repeated several times until the shell cracked on a rock and down came the lammergeier and devoured the contents. A tortoise is a round slippery object not held easily in two clumsy feet and if any attempt were made to break open the shell in the air it would inevitably lead to a drop.

I do not regard it as proved that the dropping of bones and tortoises is done with the intention of smashing them, though this often takes place.

This habit should be compared with a common habit of gulls, carrion and hooded crows which I have observed in many parts of England and Scotland; cockles and mussels are dropped from twenty to thirty feet which often—not always—cracks the shell and enables the inside to be eaten. But it is not done very intelligently; I have often seen both crows and gulls drop these shells on sand or seaweed with no effect.

The lammergeier will not approach food if vultures or even crows are feeding but prefers to wait until the carcase is abandoned and only bones left; it will swallow whole vertebrae, all small bones which it can break with ease with its powerful bill, and the skins of small mammals after the inside has been eaten (hares and hyrax). The tongue of the lammergeier is unusually long, an adaptation for licking the marrow out of bones or the brains from the skull.

Two episodes, when I saw the lammergeier at his best, remain indelibly engraved on my mind; let me quote from my diary of 26 July 1914, on the eve of the First World War, when I found myself in the mountains of Baluchistan:

The finest view I ever had of a lammergeier occurred today. I came on him but a few feet away silhouetted against a gold-red sunset, magnificent against a horizon stretching for miles and miles into golden infinity. He was quite unconscious of my presence. He sat on a rocky pinnacle facing the setting sun, wings slightly drooping and half-stretched head turned up towards heaven. Was this the phoenix of the ancients, Pliny's bird of brilliant golden plumage around the neck, the throat adorned with a crest and the head with a tuft of feathers? Was this lammergeier conscious of his sacred relationship with the sun? The phoenix of the ancients presaged peace everywhere in the land. What I saw this evening seemed to foretell war, a long, bloody war. It was the finest, most beautiful and yet most terrible, the most romantic, view of any bird I have seen at any time anywhere.

The second episode occurred on Mount Sinai where I spent the night alone in the small chapel on my fiftieth birthday. It had snowed all night, I had slept on the altar, but spent most of the night walking about to keep warm. Again from my diary:

I felt lonely and detached from the world, longing for the break of day. At last it came, first a faint blush of grey light in the east, rapidly flooding with gold. As I paced up and down in the snow the mist-soft horizon slowly revealed itself, and I felt I was living in a wilderness of spirits, lost and abandoned in the ghost-robe of dawn which enshrouded the earth. And when the sun rose over the deserts of Arabia the mist began to clear, revealing a crystal-clear ruby blaze over the eastern skies, and I looked down on one of the most beautiful sights I have ever witnessed; to the east I could see the Gulf of Aqaba and on the west I could see parts of the Gulf of Suez. On this holy mountain I felt very near to God, I turned to look at the chapel. On the small wooden cross sat a lammergeier, all hunched up in the cold but gloriously golden in the sunlight; and as I watched him, but a few yards off, his great wings spread out and he sailed forth into the gorges of those barren mountains searching for his breakfast, as his kind have done since the days of Moses.

HARRIERS

Harriers have a world-wide distribution, North and South America, Europe, Asia, Africa, Australia, New Zealand, Madagascar, and on such oceanic islands as Reunion—an even more extensive range than that of the peregrine.

All harriers employ much the same technique, hunting low over the ground with head depressed, wings above the level of the body, pouncing on any small living thing they see in scrub or reeds, avoiding forest, usually disdaining carrion, but essentially cowardly, preferring a wounded or sick animal to an active healthy one and seldom persisting if the victim fights back. Their wing area in relation to body weight is great.

MARSH HARRIER
Circus aeruginosus

I have seen many hunts and kills by the marsh harrier; on two occasions have I seen it eating carrion, once in Hungary, where a pair were eating a

PLATE 32

Korean Sea Eagle

dead horse, and once in the western desert of Egypt, where a female was eating a dead camel. On only one occasion have I seen them kill a bird as large as themselves—on the Munchar Lake in Sind, when a female turned in the air over reeds and pounced on a purple gallinule (*porphyrio*). The victim turned on its back and struck with its formidable claws and long legs, but the harrier held him by the head and neck; it was a very brief struggle.

In the Red Sea at Port Sudan I saw one defeated by a little green heron (*Butorides*) sitting in a bush in shallow water. The heron when attacked struck a threatening attitude with intention to spike the hawk with its sharp bill; the harrier hesitated and in checking its rush fell in the water with wings and tail outstretched, and the two faced each other for half a minute before the hawk pulled itself together and decided to quit.

At Jedda again when among mangrove swamp I noticed a common sand-piper feeding in the shallow water. A marsh harrier suddenly appeared and the sandpiper, being taken by surprise, dived, though the water was but a few inches deep; the harrier hovered over the spot and though I could follow the sandpiper's movements under water, the harrier seemed unable to do so and was never at the spot where it surfaced. But no sooner did the sandpiper appear than the harrier renewed its attack; after six or seven attempts it was clear the sandpiper was becoming exhausted so I ended the hunt by securing the harrier. It proved to be a most interesting bird as it was infested with eleven mallophaga of seven different species of wader feather lice, showing that its recent diet had been snatched waders.

Harriers regard owls as competitors and invariably mob them. Near the summit of Mount Kenya I witnessed what was more than a 'mob'; it was a definite attack by a female marsh harrier on a Mackinder's owl caught in the open; the owl is even larger than the hawk; the attack was pushed home and feathers flew until the owl took refuge among rocks.

Harriers will attend sportsmen and pick up wounded birds. In Sind I have seen as many as eight marsh harriers attending guns, and on the Athi Plains of Kenya I saw a single male attending a quail-shooting party; it was a pretty sight as a lanner falcon also attended, the latter striking in flight, the former pouncing on settling.

My experience of the marsh harrier is that only about one out of twelve 'pounces' is successful; but I suspect many attempts are to ascertain if the victim is wounded or sick; if the victim is active and healthy the attack is seldom pressed home. Harriers know their birds and on two occasions I have seen them swerve aside in Afghanistan when confronted by the formidable bittern.

Mrs Cowdy (*epist.*, 21 Nov. 1957) records that in Holland in May 1955 a marsh harrier was seen to alight on a coot's back, trying to lift it out of the water. After a fierce struggle the coot managed to submerge, pulling the harrier under water so that it was forced to release its hold. On surfacing, the coot was obviously distressed; meanwhile other coot had gathered in a tight bunch close by and were splashing and sending up spray as is their custom when attacked by a hawk.

In Sind I have seen marsh harriers flying low over shallow water and snatching small fish which are swallowed.

PALLID HARRIER
Circus macrourus

In habit much like other harriers; even when hungry they give up easily as the following experience shows.

At Birka in Arabia I watched a male trying to catch Lichtenstein's sandgrouse without success; this sandgrouse resents flying out from cover during daylight, resting and feeding during that time in shade and watering at dusk. This party were feeding under acacia when the harrier passed, spotted them and dashed in under the acacia, the sandgrouse, being particularly quick in taking off, getting away easily and settling again under a near-by tree; the harrier followed and was again too late; this happened again and again until the harrier gave up disgusted and turned away.

Near by was a pool of water where a green sandpiper was feeding on the edge and just below a four-foot bank. The harrier saw this new chance, deliberately turned away from the pond and then circled low so as to come over the bank exactly where the sandpiper was feeding; his pace definitely increased as he approached the spot; but he had misjudged it by about eight feet and the sandpiper flew off. Defeated twice in a few minutes, he sat on the bank looking stupidly around him. From my tent I threw him a dead sandgrouse which he enjoyed.

When he was eating this sandgrouse quite close to me, I noted that after a preliminary plucking only flesh was taken; bone, even the smallest bit, was

PLATE 33

Montagu's Harrier ♀

discarded. The soft inside is eagerly swallowed, including the stomach containing grit and seeds; thus may plants spread through the excreta or pellets of raptores.

HEN-HARRIER
Circus cyaneus

I have seen many hunts and kills of this harrier in both North and South Uist. Their technique is as other harriers, though flying slightly higher over moorland than over water or swamp.

In South Uist I was watching a harrier hunting over reeds quite close to me; the reeds were thin and full of immature coot; the harrier stooped in flight and pounced on a half-grown coot whose reaction was to turn on its back and up-splash water which so disconcerted the hawk that it failed to bind; the harrier continued to hover over his victim who attempted to scuttle off through the reeds, but the harrier bound to the coot and lifted it a foot or so from the water; but the coot was clawing and scratching furiously whenever the harrier attempted to use its bill, which technique so disconcerted the harrier that it dropped its victim and flew off.

In North Uist during snipe shooting a hen-harrier would wait on for a pricked bird and recovered three in one day.

There is no love lost between the short-eared owl and hen-harriers; there are a fair number of both in North Uist; if a harrier located an owl sitting in long grass he would at once turn aside and mob it, often making it take wing with the harrier harrying.

At Mottisfont we were often visited by a pair of these harrier, who confined their attention to water-meadow land where they played havoc with moorhen, rails, snipe, etc.

In Scotland they have been known to kill grouse, ptarmigan and partridges in level flight.

MONTAGU'S, BLACK AND PIED HARRIERS
Circus pygargus, maurus and melanoleucus

I have seen these three harriers hunting; their habits differ nowise from those of other harriers.

Montagu's harrier is perhaps the most cowardly of all. In their winter quarters in Kenya I have seen them robbed by a sparrowhawk much smaller than themselves and hesitate to tackle a lizard barely eight inches long.

I have seen the black harrier hunting in South West Africa, but without success.

The pied harrier is fairly common in northern India, Assam and Manipur in winter, when I have often observed it hunting. I have seen it snatch a wounded snipe in Assam and chasing pipits in Manipur, but without success. It is easily robbed of its prey and on one occasion was seen to be killed by an eagle. The harrier had grasped a small rail in thin reeds when, with a rush of wings, an eagle descended on it. On investigating the spot I found the rail torn to pieces, mostly eaten and the harrier lying dead—crushed and torn.

HARRIER-HAWK
Gymnogenys typicus

Seen near Budongo in Uganda when a single individual was flying low over a swamp; the flight was buoyant and graceful. This individual suddenly side-slipped into the reeds, seized its prey (probably a rail) and flew off to a near-by mound to feed.

They have the unique habit of climbing trees like a tree-creeper, with wings partly extended and tail fanned, examining holes and crevices for young birds and insects. On these occasions they search the tree from near the ground and then fly to a near-by tree for another search.

They are said to be able to move their legs forwards and backwards from the tarsal joint.

BATELEUR
Terathopius ecaudatus

This remarkable eagle, grotesque and clownish in appearance, is in reality a most dignified individual, excelling in aerobatics, intelligent and with a most affectionate nature in captivity. His harlequin plumage pattern and stump tail must not be mistaken for clownishness. His wing has twenty-five to twenty-seven secondaries, more than any other bird.

PLATE 34

Osprey at Mottisfont

When hunting they will circle or take a straight line without an apparent wing flap, sometimes at a great height and sometimes very low. Brown (*Eagles*, p. 128) estimates that the area searched for food by a bateleur in a day is some 250 square miles of country.

They will take snakes, and animals as large as hares, but I have no reliable record of them taking other birds unless sick or wounded. They come freely to carrion but refuse to consort with vultures, preferring scavenging on their own. They are bullies and pirates, robbing the secretary bird, ground hornbills and buzzard of their legitimate kills.

When I lived in Nandi (Kenya) over fifty years ago I had two pair of bateleur within my dominion. One of the pairs used to come freely to my house for scraps and by feeding them daily I got them eventually to feed within fifty yards of my house. Every morning they would 'wait on' about 300 feet up, soaring in circles with head well tucked in, finally dropping in a spiral somersault without a flap of the wing and landing within a foot of their breakfast. When both were on the ground they would bow to their meal and walk with dignity towards it, bow several times and then commence to feed. They never carried anything away.

I never saw a bateleur flap his wings when searching for food. There are two main methods of flight. The first takes the form of spiral circles, with wings well above the horizontal, and can be maintained for a considerable time. The head is not held forward or even downward but appears to be pressed against the crop in such a position that the bird appears to be looking behind it at ground already passed. A second method of flight is direct, at a great pace and apparently unassisted by gravity and without flapping, though with an occasional sway; how pace is maintained is a mystery, nor is the purpose of this direct flight clear; perhaps it is a desire to reach a new hunting-ground or to attain some favourite resting-place, on to which they will plumb-drop several hundred feet. Variations of flight are the raising of one wing and doing a 'victory roll,' presenting an almost drunken display; another variation is the clapping of wings over the back—a rare occurrence which I have seen once, performed by a single bird circling over a nest in course of construction.

Bateleur are attracted to a grass fire, usually arriving after the swifts, small hawks, bee-eaters, etc.

At Nairobi I twice witnessed bateleur taking snakes, in both cases plumb-dropping on to the victim. In one case the snake was seized behind the head, barely fifty yards from where I was sitting, and was at once lifted; the snake, a small puff-adder, struck the leg of the eagle and became firmly fixed. The eagle descended, bit through the head and sat for about five minutes watching his victim whilst still gripping him. I was anxious to obtain the snake, so fired my rifle to scare the bird; off went the bateleur and I got my snake, the eagle barking at me as it soared overhead but apparently none the worse for a bite from one of Africa's most deadly serpents. At the same place, soon afterwards, a bateleur dropped on to another snake, rose at once and commenced to feed after pulling off the head and dropping it.

When staying with my friend Ewart Grogan at his hill-top castle of Gerigan near Taveta, a pair of bateleur were usually in view from my bedroom. Returning one morning by car we ran over a large snake whose identity was unknown to me. It lay in the middle of the road, half paralysed. Halting the car about a hundred yards distant I sat down and watched, for bateleur were in the air. One soon descended, landing on the road about twenty yards from the reptile, plumage hard pressed to the body. After eyeing the snake for about two minutes, it advanced very slowly at an undignified waddle; when within a few feet from the snake the latter moved its head and neck as though to strike; the hawk's reaction was instantaneous; all plumage puffed out, wings out and a slow retreat at a waddle, but facing the snake; then commenced a series of bows and he suddenly took wing and I thought he was off, but not a bit of it; when about fifty feet up above the snake he suddenly dived on to the reptile, seized the head and after a minute or two flew off with the reptile dangling; I thought his tactics showed distinct sense.

Sir John Kennedy records (*epist.*) that one of these eagles was seen to fall to the ground and on examination a bat was found with its teeth embedded in the base of one of the wings and the main tendon bitten through; the bat was dead though its baby, clinging to its back, was alive. This occurred near Salisbury in Rhodesia in 1950.

Archer (*Birds of Somaliland*) recounts a terrific fight between two bateleur, ending in both birds crashing into a banana plantation; also a fight between a bateleur and a Verreaux's eagle.

In Kenya, motor traffic by night kills a good many hares and small mammals and an occasional bird. The bateleur has learned to patrol these roads at dawn and has become a road scavenger; they will roost on poles or trees near the road so as to be on the scene at the crack of dawn, and so soon as it is light enough to see, they start off patrolling the highway. This is a habit I have seen on the Nyeri-Nanyuki road three years in succession.

The bateleur would also attend and follow safaris in the old days of porter transport, hoping for prey disturbed by man. When crossing the northern Aberdare Mountains in 1903 I killed a large puff-adder in grassland, leaving it exposed and halting the caravan about 200 yards distant. A pair of bateleur which attended us were quick to descend and devour the corpse on the spot.

The bateleur comes freely to carrion but will not do so if kites or vultures are feeding; and yet they will rob the ground hornbill and secretary bird of their legitimate prey, these two latter species having very little means of defence.

From 1894 to 1900 my brother and I had a pair of bateleur alive at Mottisfont; they had been shipped from Delagoa Bay. After a few weeks they became very tame and enjoyed being handled, performing the double or treble bow of pleasure or gratitude in anticipation of food or head-scratching; when they wanted food they would turn their head from side to side, gazing intently at one's face, balancing the body first on one leg then on the other; but if they wanted their head scratched they would tuck it right down on their crop. Both these birds were full-winged and often enjoyed their complete liberty during the day, spending several hours on the wing but never going far, usually spiralling over the house. We only gave them their liberty when hungry, for they depended on us for food and readily came down to it when the time came to put them back into their cage.

SERPENT-EAGLE
Circaëtus gallicus

The serpent-eagle extends from the southern half of the Palaearctic Region to Cape Province. Fond of water, where it bathes and drinks more than most hawks do. Feeds almost entirely on reptiles, a common technique being to settle in a tree and browse on chameleons; when feeding on snakes or lizards it drops on them, crushing them with its powerful feet, and does not commence to feed until life is extinct; the head is sometimes discarded. A snake is grasped by the head and the writhing body of the victim does not worry the bird at all. It feeds where it kills and rarely carries its prey. They will also kill tortoises and fresh-water crabs.

Mountfort (*Portrait of a Wilderness*) writes of this eagle: 'Flies slowly, occasionally gliding on level wings, at fairly low altitude, hovering from time to time, or hanging motionless, head-on to the wind. When a snake is spotted, the eagle thrusts its head downwards, half closes its great wings and drops like a thunderbolt, seizing the wriggling prey on its outstretched talons and bearing it quickly aloft. Like the buzzard it often sits motionless for long periods, either on a tree or on the ground. In this respect one might call it rather a sluggish bird, but anyone who has seen it hunting will agree that it fully justifies its classification as an eagle.'

Mountfort also records this eagle stooping at a bee-eater in Spain. 'Suddenly there was a hissing rush of wings and I looked up just in time to see a short-toed eagle stooping at a bee-eater. The attack failed by inches. . . . The eagle's talons struck the bare branch, leaving it quivering under the impact.'

In Sinai I have seen them hover like a kestrel over a snake before dropping on to the victim.

Between Suez and Cairo there lives a colony of a large lizard, *Varanus niloticus*, which sometimes reach four feet in length. They live in burrows and if disturbed when out hunting they run back to their holes with great speed, tail in air; I was motoring to Suez one early morning and surprised one far from his burrow; he at once ran off for safety; but a serpent-eagle had also seen him and came down like an avalanche; the lizard turned to meet the attack, mouth open and looking most formidable; the serpent-eagle gained the same impression, for at the last moment he swerved off and went to sit on a mound which, as bad luck would have it, was right over *Varanus'* hole; now *Varanus* was intent on reaching safety and apparently had a great contempt for *Circaëtus*, for no sooner had the latter settled on the mound than *Varanus* continued his rush for safety. The eagle noticed his advance with agitation, puffing up his head feathers and opening his wings, and when *Varanus* was quite close to him he made a half-hearted grab at him. But *Varanus* whipped round and caught *Circaëtus* a good swipe with his tail, catching him fair and square across the body. The eagle flew off and *Varanus* disappeared underground.

I have had some experience of the tail-slash of these large lizards. During

PLATE 35

Osprey in act of diving

PLATE 36

Osprey: fish just caught

the First War a five-foot one was brought in to me. I placed it in an empty room. One of my staff entered soon afterwards with a good-sized fox terrier who at once attacked, but the terrier was swept off his legs by a single swipe and took no further interest in the reptile. Later on, when catching up this ferocious beast, I received a swipe on my legs which felt as though I had been hit by a shambok; it was distinctly painful.

It was related to me by the late Dr Flower of the Giza Zoological Gardens that he came across one of these eagles on the ground near Khartoum with a snake's head in its mouth and the body wound round the bird in such a way that he could not open his wings. The bird was captured and placed in the Khartoum Zoo.

BLACK-BREASTED HARRIER-EAGLE
Circaëtus pectoralis

Habits much the same as the serpent-eagle, feeding mainly on snakes but will take frogs and poultry. It will search ground from a considerable altitude or will still-hunt from a tree and occasionally hover like a kestrel.

Van Someren (*Fieldiana*, 1956, p. 78) records one tackling a five-foot cobra. The snake was held fast in the talons but not close enough to the head, which enabled the snake to coil round the hawk's legs and strike. Both snake and hawk were found dead, firmly locked together.

In Kenya I saw this hawk attack a snake by alighting near its victim and then advancing with head feathers puffed out and head held well back; the wings were held out with feathers scraping the ground and then with a pounce the reptile was seized by the head and carried off.

Sir R. Tredgold relates (*epist.*) that in the Umgusa Valley this eagle visited a farm every day where many chickens were kept; he collected two, one in each foot, in a single sweeping movement.

BROWN HARRIER-EAGLE
Circaëtus cinereus

I have seen this hawk catch snakes on two occasions, both in Rhodesia; in each case the snake was attacked by a sudden swoop, the snake's head being

143

grasped, causing instantaneous death, and then carried off some distance to be devoured on a tree. I recovered the head of one of these snakes and it had been crushed to a pulp.

OSPREY
Pandion haliaëtus

The diet of the osprey is almost entirely fish, both sea and fresh-water; they have been known on rare occasions to take chickens, small mammals and birds which are either sick or wounded. At Port Sudan the remains of a tufted duck were found by the nest; and at Entebbe on the Victoria Nyanza I saw an osprey settle beside a bunch of baby crocodiles who scuttled into the water with the osprey running after them; but there was no kill.

At Port Sudan I saw an osprey chase and claw a brown gannet who approached its nest. In Hampshire on the Test we were visited by an osprey for several days (see plate 34 facing p. 138); he would feed on a cattle bridge over the river; on one occasion whilst feeding, a heron came flopping up the river; the osprey abandoned his fish and flew away screaming; the heron turned and fled in the other direction; the fish dropped back into the river.

In fresh water, coarse fish are taken more readily than trout. I have no record of eels being taken.

When hunting, the osprey is fearless; I have had them diving within a few feet of a boat in Sweden and Iraq; and on the coast east of Aden I have watched them diving into surf within twenty yards of me.

In Stark and Sclater, II, p. 402, it is recorded that a lot of mullet were being hauled up on to sand when an osprey flying just overhead pounced down within four or five yards of the fishermen and seized one of the heaviest fish.

The usual technique is hovering and diving but occasionally they will swoop down from a post or tree and snatch a fish from the surface without submersion; this I have seen on Lake Huleh in Palestine. Recently in Sweden I saw an osprey snatch fish from barely eighteen inches of water; the descent was vertical with flexed wings and a fish about a foot long was seized from near the surface, the hawk's long legs allowing him to grasp without wetting his feathers.

The hover is slightly different from that of other hawks. The head is depressed, legs slightly drooping and the primaries decurved so that they point almost vertically down; hovering may last as long as twenty seconds. The final plunge is taken with retracted wings, which are almost closed when striking water, and complete submersion is the rule, head foremost but with legs drawn well forward. The highly specialised scaling of the feet ensures a tight grip, and the exterior toe is partly reversible, enabling the fish to be grasped by two claws on each side of the vertebrae. The fish is carried by both or one foot, head forwards. When the birds alight for eating, one foot is disengaged from the fish and stretched forward to assist landing.

Off Aden they have been seen diving and catching fish in surf where a man could not survive; the dive causes much spray and is not so neat as that of the gannet. On rising from the water the bird shakes himself in the air, losing height and throwing off a shower of spray. After the meal I have seen ospreys fly low over water dipping both legs and head to rid themselves of scales and slime.

On the few occasions when I have been close enough to see the detail of feeding, the throat of the fish is first attacked; the head, tail and backbone are discarded.

There is evidence to show that on occasions an osprey has been drowned by either a very heavy fish or for some reason that he could not disengage his talons. The osprey has also been known to break its wing in diving (Fisher, *U.S. Dept. Agr. Div. Orn. & Mamm.*, III, 1893). In the *Field* (20 March 1958) is a photograph of a large carp caught in Saxony to which is attached the skeleton, apparently complete, of an osprey who apparently found the fish too powerful and was dragged below and drowned. The carp is apparently some 16-17 inches long, and weighed about 10 lb. The photograph shows that fish are grasped across the dorsal ridge with both feet.

On the Victoria Nyanza as many as six ospreys can be seen fishing at one moment but they are much pirated by the African fish eagle (*Haliaëtus vocifer*). No sooner has an osprey secured a fish than one or possibly two of these eagles will attack, compelling the osprey to drop his fish in mid-air, when it is seized by the eagle before it reaches the water. The osprey cries out in protest but soon continues to fish until all the fishing eagles in the neighbourhood are satisfied.

The American bald eagle is a persistent pirate on the osprey, but on the Indus I have seen Pallas's sea-eagle and osprey fishing together in amity and in the Crimea I have seen osprey catching fish under the noses of white-tailed sea-eagles without interference from the latter.

It has been frequently stated that young ospreys take readily to fishing for themselves so soon as they leave the nest. They certainly are quick learners. My experience in Sweden (Meinertzhagen, *Ibis*, 1954, p. 153) is that the young are definitely instructed by their parents and take six days to reach proficiency in fishing.

CARACARA
Polyborus cheriway

Bent (*Bull. U.S. Nat. Mus.*, 1938, p. 133), quoting Capt. B. F. Goss, records brown pelican in Texas being attacked by caracaras when bringing food to their young, and made to disgorge. 'They did not attack out-going birds, but invariably waited for the in-coming ones, and as soon as these were over land, they pounced on them.'

Mainly a carrion feeder.

PYGMY FALCON
Polihierax semitorquatus

I became closely acquainted with this charming little falcon in Somaliland and again in South West Africa. Its usual diet is insects and small lizards. But at Sheikh in Somaliland a dove (*Oena capensis*) dashed past me with one of these small falcons in pursuit, the last phase being a rough and tumble in an acacia tree; it was a terrific struggle as the little hawk is much the same size as the dove. The hawk had hold of the dove's neck and with much wing-flapping the pair fell to the ground, the falcon on top; after a few minutes all was quiet and the falcon commenced to pluck and eat.

In South West Africa we found a pair breeding in a huge weaver colony in an acacia. The weavers showed no signs of fear though the hawks were constantly flying in and out and mixing freely with the weavers.

All hunting by these small falcons was still-hunting, not unlike that of the shrikes, the hawk sitting on a bush and descending on an insect or lizard in a gliding stoop and then returning to his stance with his prey.

PLATE 37

Greenland Falcon and Duck

THE GYR-FALCONS

Falco candicans, islandicus *and* rusticolus

Though I have seen these three races of the gyr-falcon hunting, my experiences of them are limited. Their technique appears to be flying low over ground and snatching prey as it rises or on the ground. They will still-hunt and deliberately work round so that they can approach their victim unseen.

The flight is not so accurate as that of the peregrine; they also prefer low-level hunting to stooping.

I was told by an old Greenlander in Sukkertoppen that the villagers had to give up keeping domestic pigeon as the Greenland falcons in winter would stoop at them and carry them off.

My first experience of a Greenland falcon was in January 1896 when a very white bird turned up at Mottisfont and was seen sitting on a fence-post near the Home Farm. He had a good look round, and selecting a fat Aylesbury duck waddling in the snow, flopped on to it in full view of several farm hands, carried his victim about fifty yards into snow-covered stubble and commenced to feed, screening the carcase with his outstretched wings. Some thirty people watched him at less than fifty yards. Having completed his meal he flew off. On the following morning we found him sitting beside a block on which rested a trained Greenland falcon, but all our efforts to catch him failed. George Lodge was staying with us at the time and painted the picture here reproduced.

A rather similar case occurred in South Uist when a keeper found a Greenland falcon eating one of his ducks. The bird was shot and is now stuffed at Grogarry Lodge. In Greenland the food is mainly ptarmigan and lemming, waders, especially phalarope, which are snatched as they rise from water; kittiwakes and the auk family, which are snatched from cliffs. As the prey is approached the wing beats become very rapid, the final snatch being made at over fifty miles an hour. The head of the victim is usually bitten off and the primaries removed before feeding commences.

The technique of the Iceland falcon differs in no way from that of the Greenlander. Though we saw them frequently in Iceland, all hunting was done by stalking low over the ground and snatching, or capture after a short level pursuit.

The Norwegian gyr-falcon has a similar technique; though its usual food

147

is grouse, ptarmigan, poultry, fieldfares and waders, it will kill geese, snowy owl and capercailzie.

In Swedish Lapland I had a splendid view of a gyr-falcon taking ptarmigan. The hawk was flying but a few feet above the ground when a covey of ptarmigan rose, scattering in all directions screaming and croaking. Singling out a bird, the falcon soon overtook it about twenty feet from the ground, turned in flight and came to rest with his victim not eighty yards from where I lay. He sat for about five minutes before he commenced to pluck; the head was torn off and many wing feathers removed; the meal lasted about half an hour; when satisfied he flew off, leaving quite half the bird untouched. He would possibly have returned to finish his meal later on.

J. A. Munro (*Condor*, 1936, p. 172) records a case of this falcon pursuing a mallard which alighted on ice; the falcon also landed on the ice near the duck and soon took wing and commenced to stoop at the sitting duck, trying to make it fly; but the duck refused to move and the falcon felt unable to tackle a duck sitting on ice; I fancy a peregrine would have done so.

These falcons have been driven from a ternery by a concentrated mob of terns and they are often mobbed by both ravens and skuas, paying less attention to ravens than to the latter. Gyrs avoid skuas; the latter have a more rapid flight and greater agility on the wing.

In the old days when falconry was a sport commonly practised in Britain and Holland, gyr-falcons were in great demand for hawking heron; the trained falcon usually struck the wing or body of the heron, avoiding the head on account of the formidable beak. But a heron does not know how to use his beak when in flight though, if driven to earth, he becomes a most dangerous quarry and by stabbing could easily kill his tormentor. I have never seen a wild falcon attack a heron, nor can I find any record of either gyrs or peregrines doing so; but I have, in Hampshire, seen a peregrine playing with a heron, stooping but not striking, the heron being unable to turn over on its back, as hawks can do, so that the formidable bill can be used.

In Tudor times, when the red kite (*Milvus*) was common in Britain, gyrs were entered to them; this was indeed a noble sport and gave rise to J. Wolf's famous picture, originally painted for Lord Lilford at a cost of 500 guineas and sold, when the contents of Lilford Hall were auctioned, for £9. A photograph of it is here reproduced by kind permission of its present owner, Mr C. W. Scott of Laidlawstiel.

PLATE 38

Gyr-Falcons and Red Kite

LANNER
Falco biarmicus

Comparing my own experiences of the lanner and peregrine when hunting, I should say the lanner is less enterprising than the peregrine; they stoop less and prefer a level chase, their stoops are less accurate and they are not so persistent; I believe their quarry is almost always smaller than that of the peregrine.

My friend Jack Mavrogordato has a higher opinion of the lanner; he tells me:

One of my wild-caught lanners got so good at the game that he would from a pitch of 200–300 feet, knock down a great grey shrike, first shot, before it had gone more than a few feet; and another killed several September partridges in Norfolk. In my experience I would say that the main difference between the stoop of a lanner and of a peregrine was not accuracy and not even speed, but force of impact; the peregrine hits harder because size for size, he has more weight behind him; i.e. the proportion of body weight to wing is much greater in the peregrine than in the lanner or saker. I remember one of my lanners after a long flight in England at a domestic pigeon, manœuvring himself into position for a vertical stoop at it, and then hitting it so hard (first shot) that the pigeon fell like a stone to the ground 100 ft. or so below and bounced off it like a tennis ball, stone dead; and a lanner is not much heavier than a pigeon.

When I was staying on an ostrich farm near Middelburg (Cape) in 1907, my host complained of a falcon trying to snatch newly hatched chicks, usually appearing on the scene about an hour after daylight. On the morning of my departure this falcon appeared in a steep glide to where a female ostrich was standing over her chicks; it was a lanner; she did not attempt to get in under the ostrich where the chicks were huddled together, but contented herself with stooping at the hen ostrich, whose reaction was to throw back her head and neck so that it lay on her back; in this posture she faced the lanner whenever she stooped; after about twenty stoops the lanner went off; my host assured me that this game went on almost every morning.

When on the summit of Mount Carmel I was attracted by the pitiful cries of a small bird high up in the heavens; a lanner was pursuing a pipit, turning and twisting in all directions. The pipit finally made a dive to earth, but too late, as the falcon stooped and seized it in his stride.

At the Pyramids in Egypt I saw a hoopoe defeat a lanner high up in the heavens, the victim apparently being able to climb quicker than the hawk.

I have seen a song thrush defeat a lanner in the open in Palestine by quicker twisting in flight, the lanner finally abandoning the chase after about five minutes' activity.

At Aden they have been seen feeding on small fruit bats at dusk, eating them in the air after removing the wings.

In South Africa they have been seen feeding on locusts and following shooting parties to pick up wounded birds. In the early days of the Uganda Railway I have seen lanners flying alongside a train near Voi and hunting rollers and doves as they were disturbed from the telegraph wires. And when porter transport was the rule, my caravan has been attended on more than one occasion by a pair of lanner hoping for disturbed birds. In the Hoggar Mountains of the Central Sahara a pair of lanner attended our camp every morning at about 9 a.m., circling around for a few minutes in a futile search for disturbance.

SAKER
Falco cherrug

JUGGER
Falco jugger

I treat these falcons together, as on the many occasions when I have seen them hunting, procedure has been similar.

A slower wing-beat than the peregrine and usually taking smaller prey, more often on the ground than in the air. They will still-hunt, sitting on telegraph poles or trees, or even on a mound, approaching their victim flying low and fast, binding to and crushing, and not striking with the hind claw, as does the peregrine. I have seen them stalking sandgrouse at water, flying but a few inches above ground level, selecting a victim, and after a slight rough and tumble securing a bird which has always been eaten where killed; the victim is seized by the neck and strangled.

Mavrogordato (*epist.*) witnessed a similar stalk of a pair of sandgrouse in long grass away from water in the Sudan; the sandgrouse rose just in time and the saker almost immediately abandoned the hunt.

Trained saker will readily attack wild geese and large bustard (*Hoobara*), binding to the neck until the falconer comes up to help them. Geese, when so attacked, will remain on the ground, concentrate and try to defend themselves by pecking and I have seen a hawk driven off injured before the falconer comes up.

150

PEREGRINE

Falco peregrinus

The peregrine has a global though continental distribution from the circumpolar Arctic to Patagonia, Cape Province and Australia; not in New Zealand.

Throughout their range they are primarily bird-killers. Food is very varied and probably each pair or even individual may have its own choice, depending on what it was entered to by its parents. But of course when hungry, little comes amiss. Birds as small as pipits and as large as a barnacle goose have been recorded, whilst in Alaska large gulls appear to form the bulk of the food—over 19 per cent (Cade, *Auk*, 1951, p. 373). In Britain, coastal peregrines feed mainly on jackdaws, rock pigeon and the smaller gulls, whilst inland the smaller game birds—grouse and partridges, duck, the thrush family and waders—appear to form the bulk of food taken. It is astonishing how frequently peregrines will kill kestrel, the American sparrowhawk (*Falco sparverius*), owls and the European sparrowhawk (*Accipiter nisus*). There are two records of raven and the greater black-backed gull being killed, and an attempt to kill a hen-harrier. Anton Schweigman (*epist.*) records a peregrine killing a black-throated diver (*Gavia arctica*) in flight near Rossitten. Very rarely mammals are taken, the size ranging from hares to shrews, and occasionally they have been seen catching large insects in the air where they are devoured.

The shaheen (*F. babylonicus*) mostly takes birds in flight, small Passerines, swifts, bee-eaters, etc., but will also catch rock pigeon, chukar, sandgrouse and duck; they have also been recorded preying on geese and bats (Dementiev, *Ibis*, 1957, p. 481). In Khartoum during locust invasions this small peregrine feeds greedily on this pest, consuming them in the air.

This same falcon, when trained, has been driven off its kill on Salisbury Plain by a pair of crows (Mavrogordato, *epist.*).

In level flight a peregrine will bind to the victim, seizing neck or body and carrying; or it will sometimes turn underneath its prey and seize the stomach; but these techniques are only used with birds considerably less than its own weight. The normal method is a stoop at terrific speed, when the victim is hit with either one or both hind claws; the probable aim is the head or neck, in which case the head of the victim has been known to fall a hundred yards from the body; but more often the victim is disabled by a deep gash on the back or by a broken wing.

A peregrine's technique is so varied that I give some cases I have witnessed.

In Arabia in 1948 I came across eight of the large chukar (*Alectoris melanocephala*) watering in a close bunch in the open. A peregrine came up the wadi, catching them in the open; the chukar crouched; the hawk made shallow stoops at them on the ground; these proving ineffectual, he settled about twenty yards from them; but some inquisitive baboon approached, jabbering and fussing to such an extent that the falcon flew off; how that attack might have ended is uncertain.

In Hampshire I have seen a peregrine stoop at a covey of partridges to try and make them rise, but after each stoop, and during the time the hawk was preparing for his next stoop, the partridges would move slightly nearer some dense bushes until they were so close as to run off into them before the hawk could turn. I have also seen a peregrine alight in heather and deliberately hunt for grouse which refused to fly, and eventually catch one on the ground.

As a boy I lived in the Test Valley. In hard weather duck of all sorts would congregate on flooded land and ponds and these duck were always accompanied by a pair of peregrine; every evening they harried the duck, preferring wigeon to mallard or teal. Killing was carried out by stoop, always over dry land, and the pair of hawks were amazingly successful, rarely failing at their first attempt. In the still frosty air we always heard a resounding smack as the hawk struck and then watched the spiral dive to the dead victim lying in the water meadow.

I have on several occasions seen peregrine after teal but never with complete success. On the first occasion, in Kenya, the teal just managed to dive into reeds at such speed that he was temporarily stunned and was caught. On the second occasion, in Baluchistan, a teal, closely followed by a peregrine, dived at full speed into deep water; the hawk banked, hovered over the spot and picked up the teal from the surface when he showed and flew off with it. The third occasion was in Caithness, when a peregrine stooped at a small party of teal in a peat pond surrounded by buck-bean and reeds. The hawk continued to hover over the teal who were more terrified of the peregrine than they were of us, for nothing would induce them to rise even when a dog was put in after them. They were quacking their poor souls out. On the following day we saw a peregrine stoop at and bind to a grouse. One of the covey lost its head and dived headlong into thick heather whence he was picked up half-stunned.

On a cold clear November day I was on the summit of Mount Hekla in South Uist; much cackling announced the autumn arrival of hundreds of barnacle geese flying high overhead at about 5,000 feet, and a pair of peregrine seemed to be amusing themselves by stooping at them, whether in earnest or play we shall never know, but the geese considered it serious, and many side-slipping or with almost vertical dive descended to Loch Bee, the two hawks continually harassing them right down to water level.

Roberts (*Brit. B.*, 1946, p. 318) records a case of a peregrine dropping vertically with extended legs on to young redshank crouching in grass and making off with the chick.

Leach (*Field*) records a falcon stooping at a wigeon and breaking its wing, the latter falling into shallow water. The falcon made eleven unsuccessful attempts to snatch the duck who was diving to avoid capture, and at the twelfth attempt succeeded and carried it off.

The late Archibald Thorburn told me many years ago that he had been commissioned to paint a peregrine stooping at an ostrich, an event which his patron, who lived in Scotland, had himself witnessed in South Africa. I regarded this as an extravaganza at the time, but recently in Kenya I saw a peregrine trying to capture a chick ostrich whose mother was defending it. An ostrich's weapon is her leg, with which she can strike mortal blows, and the old lady was dancing round kicking wildly at the bird which was trying to catch one of the many chicks all clustered round her feet. The peregrine failed, his final effort, which was pure spite, being directed at the head of the hen ostrich; she did not seem to mind that, laying her head back between her wings.

In Cornwall I have seen peregrine still-hunting, perched on a cliff and waiting for unsuspecting jackdaws to pass, when they would dash out and almost always secure their prey. I have also seen them flying along a cliff-face in Orkney snatching rock pigeon or fulmar caught unawares in the open.

Sprunt (*Auk*, 1951, p. 373) gives a remarkable account of the American peregrine feeding on bats in Texas. I quote:

The method of securing prey varies. At times, the falcon will dive headlong into the stream of bats in a spectacular stoop; again, it may fly straight through the 'living river' and emerge with a bat in the talons. Also, at times, it flies parallel with them, then swerves sideways, makes a 'zoom' and reaches outward and forward with the talons, to seize a bat. One was seen to miss such a strike, then, almost instantaneously, reach sideways with the right foot and seize a bat.

In several instances the falcon was seen to begin feeding on the bat at once. Reaching the foot forward and the head downward and back, it devoured the edible portions quickly, releasing the wings which fluttered downward; during this manœuvre the bird was soaring.

The population of Ney Cave (where this account was witnessed) is said to contain from 20 to 30 million bats.

Corbett (*Temple Tiger*, p. 127) gives a vivid description of a 'ground owl' spiralling up and up when chased by a falcon and eventually eluding pursuit by gaining the shelter of a cloud, the pursuer gliding back to the tree whence he started.

At Hoy in Orkney the falcon of a nesting pair was a puffin-killer in the summer; she lived in perfect amity with three pair of great skua who were also puffin-killers. I witnessed three kills by the falcon; she would 'wait on' for puffins returning home with their beaks festooned with sand-eels and stoop down on them once they had topped the high cliffs. Though the stoops would have been easier for her over the sea, she always waited for her victim to be well on the land side of the cliff-edge.

An officer travelling in Tibet has recorded to me that a hoopoe, which was being pursued in open country by a falcon, took refuge on his saddle and refused to leave, though handled, until the hawk sheered off.

Mr Mavrogordato tells me that he has seen a peregrine completely defeated by a hoopoe crossing the Nile at Omdurman and miles from shelter of any sort; and that he has seen the smaller (*babylonicus*) peregrine fail in several stoops against the golden sparrow.

When at Hoy in Orkney we constantly had a pair of breeding peregrine round the house. I had a splendid cloth kite shaped like a bird complete with eagle's head and tail. I used to fly it from the house, letting it rise to about 500 feet. It never failed to attract one or both of the hawks, who would play around and stoop at it; on one occasion the falcon actually ripped the cloth of a wing. By releasing the strain on the cord I could make the kite nose-dive; this caused great excitement and would result in both hawks stooping. On another occasion a hen-harrier joined them but was at once driven off. The sight of a stooping hawk is tremendously exciting to other predators, as it suggests piracy, especially among certain eagles.

There is also a rare technique which I have only twice seen, once against a plover (*Vanellus*) and once against a black-headed gull (*ridibundus*). I call it the 'cross-over attack and defence.' I have never seen the opening move, but when operating the two birds are poised opposite each other, the prospective victim slightly higher than the hawk; they then stoop towards each other and when almost contacting the victim suddenly side-slips, up-slips or down-slips. The hawk never knows which. And they then face each other, the victim still slightly higher than the hawk and having taken each other's places; and so the game goes on until, in both cases observed, the hawk tires and gives up.

On two occasions I have seen peregrines kill in the air, the victim dropping on dry land and the hawk not bothering to feed; in one case a starling and in the second instance a rock pigeon (*livia*); both in Cornwall.

The trained peregrine has been entered to the sarus crane, a bird standing five feet high and with a powerful bill. Here is an account of the flight taken from *Falconry in the Valley of the Indus* (1852):

There they went, the crane heavily flapping, then shooting up perpendicularly as an arrow, and the hawk circling after her, narrowing the sweep, and following the quarry with the eye of a greyhound. Now the sarus is tired out; she can rise no more; the hawk is on a level with her. Ha! she screams; the hawk is above her; sudden death is near her. Again she shrieks shrilly; she knows that the swoop is coming, her only chance is to face the foe with her sharp stout beak. Now the hawk stoops; the crane has escaped this once, by bending back her neck; the falcon must tire her out with twenty sham attacks. Between fright and fatigue the crane can scarcely move. At last the hawk holds her, blinding her with his talons; they tumble through the air; they spread out their wings as they reach the earth. It was a splendid sight.

In February 1913 on a sheet of water near Meerut I saw eleven peregrine harrying duck who were loath to leave the surface. We were there to shoot, the falcons were there to hunt. The duck were loath to take wing but were forced to do so by beaters. We co-operated in the ducks' discomfiture. It was a beautiful sight seeing the falcons stooping in all directions and paying scant regard to the fusillade. I counted five strikes, all over water and all recovered by the falcons.

Large airfields are an attraction to many birds—gulls, plover, rooks, starlings, etc. During the Second World War these birds became a menace to planes landing and taking off. Trained falcons were suggested to scare birds away; but peregrines cannot be trained to chase only and not to kill. And if the hawk fails to kill he may fly long distances and get lost; moreover, a hawk entered to rooks will look askance at gulls. The experiment was not a success, probably due to the fear engendered by a hawk being purely temporary; once the falcon is grounded the birds return. It would be necessary to maintain a continuous patrol of hawks during the hours of daylight with at least one falcon always in the air on every aerodrome. This would have entailed an impossible number of falcons—and falconers.

Rudebeck (*Oikos*, 1951, pp. 206-16) gives nineteen accounts of successful kills out of 260 hunts observed. Mavrogordato (*epist.*) using trained falcons in the Sudan thought that only one in four chases ended in a kill.

Resident peregrines have regular plucking-grounds to which the victim is taken if not too heavy; the spot chosen is either on a prominent branch of a tree or some rocky outcrop; even in their winter quarters birds have been seen to use the same post every day for feeding.

A female peregrine can lift a wigeon over a distance of half a mile; the peregrine weighing about 800 grammes and an average wigeon the same—a remarkable achievement.

During the incubation period the tiercel has been seen approaching the nest with food whilst the falcon would fly out a short distance and receive the food in the air. In Ross-shire I have seen this happen well out to sea away from the cliff-face where the eyrie was.

A peregrine can attain a speed of 65 miles an hour on the level and possibly up to 165 and over when stooping. Level flight cannot be undertaken for more than about a mile; after a thousand-yard chase I have seen a tiercel so out of breath that he could not feed. And I have seen a level flight after sandgrouse abandoned after only half a mile. When not hunting, a peregrine was timed by speedometer (Mavrogordato, *epist.*) and attained 30-35 m.p.h.

TAITA FALCON
Falco fasciinucha

This rare falcon, little larger than a hobby, occurs in the more arid regions of East Africa. The only record of its predations was recounted to me by the late Blaney Percival, who shot a specimen at Voi in Kenya as it was killing tame pigeon by follow-chase.

John Williams has seen one chasing *Quelea* in low level flight. A pair at

PLATE 39

Taita Falcon

the Victoria Falls were often seen hunting at tree-top level, obviously using the surprise-and-grab technique.

MERLIN
Falco columbarius

The merlin breeds in the northern parts of the Holarctic Region, south to the mouth of the Volga and east to Japan; further south in winter but scarcely reaching the tropics. Food is almost entirely small birds but is said to feed largely on lemmings where they occur.

They are lively, audacious, marvellously active and usually fly close to the ground. They also have an impertinent side to their character. I witnessed a cock merlin in Mull chasing a meadow pipit which took refuge between the legs of a grazing cart-horse. There was a scurry and chase between the legs of the horse who strongly resented the scrimmage about its person; but the pipit escaped; the merlin flew away disgusted, but after going about twenty yards suddenly turned and deliberately struck the poll of the horse, causing it to throw up its head in alarm; having accomplished this act of spiteful bad manners the merlin flew off. This act reminds me of a story related by an eccentric gentleman I met at lunch with Lord Allenby in Sinai during the First World War. He said with great seriousness that he had seen a merlin strike a cart-horse senseless to the ground. Allenby, with a twinkle in his eye but with great seriousness, said that his experience had been that when anger entered into the soul of a wild animal, it became irresponsible, for in South Africa he had seen a wild cat, disturbed in its siesta by a large bull giraffe, pounce on the enormous beast, climb rapidly up its neck and tear its throat out.

Rudebeck (*Oikos*, 1951, p. 202) has recorded 155 hunts by merlins, only 5 per cent of which were successful. I have observed well over a hundred hunts in Iceland, Scandinavia, Scotland, Cornwall, Egypt, Germany and Yorkshire and of these fifteen were successful.

The merlin is particularly audacious and will attack the golden eagle if it approaches its nest, repeatedly stooping at the great bird and on one occasion forcing it to turn over on its back. In Yorkshire I witnessed an audacious attack on a raven. As we lunched, a pair of merlin flew round us in great excitement. A solitary raven crossed their path, croaking contentedly to himself and little suspecting the storm which awaited him. No sooner did he enter the merlins' territory than they both went for him, harrying him and making him turn on his back to defend himself. The raven lost height so rapidly that he soon came to earth where he took refuge under a boulder whence he peeped out, croaking with anger. The cock merlin sat on a rock near by and remained there for some time, the raven peeping out to watch his tormentor, croaking wildly. And so we left them, the raven a prisoner, the small hawk triumphant, with its head on one side, revelling in his daring impertinence (see plate 40 facing p. 161).

The merlin's prey is almost entirely taken on the wing and comprises small Passerines, though doves, insects and small rodents have been recorded and, in the Arctic, the lemming. It is a bird of open country, flying at great speed close to the ground and showing skill in stalking and surprising individuals and flocks. At the Delta Barrage in Egypt I came across a party of several merlin resting on spring passage in a dense-foliaged tree. As I watched a single bird flew out, seized a bulbul and was back in the tree in less than a minute. Then another and another merlin flew out, and with marvellous accuracy and rapidity took an unsuspecting victim, returning to the tree for a leisurely meal. No attack lasted more than a minute and I must have seen six to eight successful hunts in less than an hour.

On two occasions have I seen deliberate and very successful stalks. In North Uist in October I was watching a redshank feeding on tidal water close to grass-covered sand dunes. A merlin crossed the estuary some three hundred yards from the redshank, flying very low, and as soon as the hawk was out of sight of the redshank it turned and came up behind me at increased speed, exactly opposite the redshank and topping the grass-covered dune. He was but twenty yards from the unsuspecting redshank which was seized almost before it took wing and carried off before it had time to utter more than a single 'kititit.' The redshank was taken and carried off in full flight for about a mile, when the merlin landed behind a stone wall, mobbed by plover and meadow pipits. A merlin weighs just over 200 grammes and a redshank from 120 to 130 grammes; this is the largest bird I have seen a merlin kill and carry.

Another successful stalk was seen in Ross-shire. A flock of siskin were feeding near some alder bushes. A cock merlin passed them at about a hundred yards' distance without apparently noticing them, but when out of sight of the siskin suddenly turned and, flying very low and fast, dashed in on them almost before they realised the danger, seized one as it scurried for safety and went off with it.

On moorland the meadow pipit is the usual victim and is usually surprised in flight. Then follows some quick aerobatics in which the merlin is not always successful; he will suddenly abandon the chase and continue hunting or the pipit will get into long heather; sometimes the merlin will alight and search, sometimes he cannot be bothered and goes off.

When hunting meadow pipits in the air close to the ground, the hunt usually ends in a kill or the pipit gaining the heather and escaping. But sometimes the pipit gains altitude and the chase of sudden turns and twists at great speed continues far up to almost out of sight. This sometimes ends in capture, sometimes in exhaustion of either hawk or prey. I have never made up my mind whether the pipit is purposely driven up by the merlin or whether the pipit deliberately gains height to avoid a stoop.

I have seen a hen merlin hunting baby grouse on the ground with the mother displaying and fussing, making mock attacks on the hawk; but the merlin paid not the slightest attention to the mother and would sometimes completely disappear in the long heather; but she never got one of those babies and eventually went off hungry.

Geyr (*Orn. Monatsb.*, L, p. 1) records a merlin flying within a flock of swallows who evinced no fear of their dangerous companion; the hawk seized a victim and made off. In Egypt I have seen a merlin dash through a party of screaming swallows, seize one in his stride and make off.

In South Uist I witnessed an unsuccessful attack by a merlin on a snipe. The hawk was flying fast just above ground level when a snipe rose in front of it, making off at great speed and rising. The hawk gave chase but a snipe can rise much quicker than a merlin who was soon outdistanced and gave up.

In Estonia I saw a merlin stalk and attack a flock of woodlark on arable land and far from cover; but the larks kept their heads and crouched instead of taking wing; the merlin came to rest on the ground near the larks, who at once rose and flew some twenty yards towards forest when they again settled. The merlin was defeated, for over short distances he could never get up sufficient speed; if any lark had made an attempt at prolonged flight, his doom would have been sealed; but as it was, these successful tactics enabled the larks to reach the shelter of the forest and the hawk was defeated by an intelligence superior to his own.

Williamson (*Scot. Nat.*, 1953, p. 56) records a merlin on Fair Isle failing to kill a hoopoe, the latter being able to climb quicker than the hawk. See also under the lanner falcon and sparrowhawk. Hawks appear to favour hoopoes. Are they attracted by brilliant plumage? Have they an aesthetic sense, the bright plumage enhancing the taste of the flesh? Mavrogordato suggests that hoopoes, with their apparently slow, floppy flight, look so easy that the hawk, even after several failures, is tempted to have another try.

McClure (*Auk*, 1957, p. 101) describes an attack by a merlin on bulbuls (*Ixos amaurotis*) in Japan. The hawk attacked the flock, which wheeled and circled about some trees. The flock never attempted to enter the trees but flew around them and over them as though to confuse the hawk, who was trying to isolate an individual from the flock, which was a hundred feet above ground but being slowly manœuvred to ground level. After about three minutes an individual swung too far out of the flock and was at once seized and carried off.

Though food is usually small birds they have been known to take woodcock and ptarmigan. They have also entered pigeon lofts and seized pigeons. Hine (*Ohio Journ. Sci.*, 1919, p. 475) records an encounter between a merlin and a magpie (*Pica*) in Alaska, the latter avoiding capture.

Small rodents and even rabbits are rarely taken.

The hobby frequently kills for fun. I have only once observed a merlin do so—in Cornwall. The hawk was flying low in stone-wall country when it surprised some skylarks who at once took wing—very stupidly. One was seized in the air, carried some twenty yards and dropped. The hawk then sat on a stone wall, head cocked on one side, contemplating its kill, which lay dead but ten yards away. The hawk remained in contemplation for some ten minutes, then, forgetting about the lark, commenced to preen and scratch itself, finally making off unconcerned at this senseless act of slaughter.

SOOTY FALCON
Falco concolor

The main diet is insects, lizards, bats and small birds obtained by low flying and snatching. Fifty years ago a pair resided at Mombasa Fort where bats were taken in the evening. In Egypt they take bats, sandgrouse coming to

PLATE 40

Raven and Merlin

drink, and migrant bee-eaters; they have been seen to stoop like a peregrine in Egypt.

ELEONORA'S FALCON
Falco eleonorae

Eleonora's falcon is common on the islands off Crete and on Mogador Island off Morocco. Their technique is still-hunting in preference to flight-hunting though they will often fly low over the ground surprising their victims. I have never seen an Eleonora stoop. On Mogador Island they are in large numbers, a regular colony of several dozen birds, sitting about the rocks and waiting for their victims to come to them. They live on the south side in spring to catch the northbound migrants and in autumn they keep to the north side to catch the southbound birds. But in both Crete and Morocco they will when hungry come to the mainland where they scour the country from low elevations, surprising their prey. In Crete I saw one follow a blackbird into a bush, drive it out and then secure it by a follow-chase. Lynes records that the favourite food of Eleonora's falcon in the Aegean Islands is the hoopoe during the migratory season.

HOBBY
Falco subbuteo

The hobby is both enterprising and wonderfully quick in his movements. In pursuit of birds he will both stoop and engage in a follow-chase. In the case of small birds he will strike and carry, often devouring his victim, sometimes as large as a starling, in mid-air. I have also seen migrating hobbies, accompanied by flocks of whirling starlings apparently in friendly rivalry, circling about and catching insects in mid-air and hold them to the beak for eating. The crop of one of these birds was stuffed with the succulent bodies of his prey but not a single wing was observed, these being discarded in flight.

The hobby is not averse to killing for the love of slaughter. I have seen a single bird kill two house martins in quick succession and drop them; and in Ladak I have seen a pair of hobbies deliberately indulging in useless slaughter with small finches and wagtails, dropping their prey when killed; not a nice habit but no doubt affording infinite amusement to the hobby.

A hobby will not tolerate being mobbed. I have seen eagles, peregrines, goshawk, harriers and all sorts of owls being mobbed, but the hobby will not tolerate it and turns at once on his tormentors. I have seen meadow pipits and blackbirds try to mob hobbies and in every case the hobby turned on them at once, chasing them even through trees and catching them up. 'The hobby is itself a terrific mobber. Nesting hobbies will mob trained peregrines and actually strike them on the back. I once made use of this habit to trap one, using nooses on the back of the peregrine' (Mavrogordato, *epist.*).

At Mottisfont we had a pair of hobbies breeding annually on the estate and another pair near by at Danebury. We often saw them dash right through house martins or swallows, seizing a bird in flight without stoop or check. The largest bird we saw them take was a turtle dove, caught in level flight and carried some distance. In the mayfly season, a hobby would occasionally come down to the Test to feed on these succulent insects, catching and eating them in the air. Small birds are sometimes eaten in the air, the legs and head being discarded, a most wasteful method.

Moule (*Brit. B.*, 1952, p. 418) records a pair of hobbies pursuing two green woodpeckers, flying alongside them; but the woodpeckers reached shelter in safety. A green woodpecker has a formidable bill and no doubt would cause some hesitation on the hawk's part.

In Ladak I witnessed two hobbies chasing a pair of hoopoe, binding to and releasing them again or sometimes bringing them to the ground and contemplating their feat with satisfaction, then suddenly taking the air again and repeating the process on some other unfortunate.

In Afghanistan I witnessed a small flock of migrating hobbies catching termites in the air, discarding the wings and feeding direct from foot to mouth.

On two occasions in Ladak I saw a hobby chasing swifts without success. A German observer (quoted by Lack, *Swifts in a Tower*, p. 20) found that of sixty-seven birds taken by hobbies, as many as twenty-six were swifts, probably weakened by under-nourishment or cold. Lack (*op. cit.*, p. 201) records a swift entangled by its sharp claws in a hobby.

I believe the hobby, where food is abundant, to be largely crepuscular in feeding habit. In Hungary where I watched a roosting place of a few birds in autumn, they were certainly only active in the late afternoon.

Reutervall (*Var Fagelv*, 1955, p. 89) records common terns and common gulls in southern Sweden making a combined attack on a hobby and drowning it.

LESSER KESTREL
Falco naumanni

The diet of the lesser kestrel is mainly insects. In Iraq I saw one come down and settle beside a wounded sandgrouse, remaining thus for half an hour before he decided to leave it. There are very few records of lizards, small birds or mammals. Mavrogordato tells me that he has seen one caught in Khartoum with a live sparrow as decoy.

At Acre in Palestine I counted 78 and 44 centipedes in the crops of two birds. In Kenya the crops of two males on passage contained over 140 bodies of flying termites. Throughout locust-infested areas the lesser kestrel feeds on both hoppers and flying insects, often becoming so gorged that flight is difficult.

When eating hoppers they will stand on the ground picking them up. Flying locusts are caught by the feet in the air, the wings torn off by passing the insect to the mouth and the body then swallowed, the bird gliding all the while. But except when feeding on swarming insects, hunting is done by hovering and a quick descent with almost closed wings.

KESTREL
Falco tinnunculus

The kestrel has a varied diet, rarely small birds and mammals, usually lizards, beetles, small insects and even worms. The usual method of hunting is by hover and drop, sometimes by still-hunting and glide and very rarely by follow-chase.

Birds as large as adult turtle doves, half-grown partridges, starlings and missel-thrush have been recorded. Parker and Summers (*Brit. B.*, 1956, p. 180) record as many as twenty-four juvenile starlings being fed to a brood of kestrels. Bats have also been recorded. Occasionally carrion—rabbit's guts. The food ratio of small mammals to birds is about 65 to 8 per cent in Britain.

Abroad, the bird diet tends to become smaller and the insect and lizard diet larger. In Egypt I have removed a lizard, eighteen beetles and seven grasshoppers from a single male. The tree-creeper has been recorded as the prey of the kestrel though it is difficult to see how it was caught. In Egypt a dead kestrel with a dead poisonous snake coiled round it was found by Nicoll.

Mr Gordon Turnill (*epist.*, 26 Sept. 1957) records a female kestrel descending on to a wounded partridge only a few yards from guns and beaters.

Tubbs (*Brit. B.*, 1952, p. 424) records a flock of pigeon mobbing a flying kestrel, buffeting it in their midst and not releasing it until they split up.

In *Nature* (1953, p. 243) there is a suggestion that kestrels hunt by sound as well as by sight, based on a bird circling round a buzzing insulator. See also under short-eared owl.

RED-LEGGED FALCON
Falco vespertinus

Both the nominate form and the eastern race (*amurensis*) have similar habits, hovering like the kestrel, catching small lizards and insects on the ground; they will also fly round in graceful circles when termites are in the air, catching and eating them on the wing; they have also been observed taking dragonflies; small mammals have also been included in their prey; they have been seen snatching water-beetles from water. Occasionally captures small birds and is known to have taken chicks from a farm.

Flocks in Africa have a preference for feeding at dusk when flying insects are more abundant.

In Estonia I saw a solitary male sitting on a telegraph post whence he frequently flew when an insect took the air. He also glided down from his stance some 150 yards, returning with a small mouse which he ate on the post. When feeding on the ground on locust hoppers they can run with considerable speed, and I have seen a whole flock in South Africa in grass a foot high, running hither and thither after insects.

When in the air hawking insects they are often in company with the lesser kestrel and bee-eaters without any sign of aggressive competition.

165

PLATE 41

Hoopoe nesting at Thebes

N. STREKALOVSKY

AUTOLYCISM

BIRDS: MAKING USE OF MAN

THIS chapter deals with the use birds make of man, his buildings, ships, habits, etc., and the use birds make of other birds, mammals, reptiles and fish. The expression 'parasitism'—strictly speaking eating beside another, but also a partnership between two organisms which is detrimental to one partner and beneficial to the other; commensalism, involving living as another's tenant; and symbiosis, where both parties receive advantage from association—none of these adequately express the purpose of this subject.

I therefore use the word *Autolycism*.

Autolycus was an Athenian, a hanger-on from interested motives, a picker-up of small trifles, a scrounger who was notorious for making use of others. It is a vice often met with in the human race, and its study among animal groups other than birds would be a most fascinating work, for they all in some form or other make use of others; in fact, the deeper one probes the more one realises the dependence of almost every form of life on some other form of life.

For many years I have been collecting notes on Autolycism, and these were almost in publishing condition when Miriam Rothschild and Theresa Clay published their excellent and most readable *Fleas, Flukes and Cuckoos* (Collins, 1952), which has stolen much of my thunder; but there still remains sufficient to justify a further contribution on the subject.

I shall not touch on the manner in which birds have been influenced by man's activities on the land—agriculture, built-up areas, draining of marshes, construction of reservoirs, deforestation and afforestation; these have been dealt with by Nicholson (*Birds and Man*, 1951) very fully and with greater competence than I am capable of.

Use of man by birds

The direct use of man by birds, in its crudest form, is exemplified by a tree-creeper (*Certhia*) using a man as a tree and running up his legs. I experienced the same type of use in the Bois de Boulogne when a young woodpecker (*Dendrocopos*), recently out of his nest and unable to fly, hopped towards me, climbed up my leg and body, along my outstretched arm and on to the tree where his parents awaited him. There are many cases of kingfishers (*Alcedo atthis*) perching on fishermen's rods and of swallows (*Hirundo*) taking a fisherman's fly. And there is the case of the Galapagos flycatcher assaulting David Lack several times in an effort to collect his hair as nesting material.

In the following notes there is a certain amount of repetition from notes on *Pirates and Predators*; better to repeat than repeated cross-references.

Use of buildings, etc.

The use of human habitation by birds is widespread; the custom can only have been started comparatively recently and has spread rapidly. Birds regard human habitations as conglomerations of cliffs and boulder-strewn hill slopes; they cannot realise their vulnerability due to staircases and windows. The use of human habitations has a marked effect on wildness, converting some of the wildest birds to some of the tamest. Fitter (*London's Natural History*, 1945) gives innumerable cases of this type in London.

The raven (*Corvus corax ruficollis*) often nests in ruined buildings throughout its range. The carrion crow (*Corvus corone*) breeds regularly in inner London and has become so tame that it may be seen feeding within a few yards of screaming, playing children. There are several cases of the carrion crow breeding on houses.

The hooded crow (*C. cornix*) in Egypt, Iraq and Stockholm is a town dweller and would doubtless join the proletariat in Scotland if it would behave itself; many cases of both carrion and hooded crows nesting on telegraph poles and signal posts are given in *Brit. B.*, 1956, p. 180.

Rooks (*C. frugilegus*) nested on the Tower of London at the beginning of the nineteenth century, and when I was a boy there was a large rookery where now stands the North Thames Gas Board in Church Street, Kensington. There was a rookery in the Inner Temple Gardens in 1914. There is a vast rookery on a church in Denmark housing over 200 pair. They have nested on electric pylons and among girders of a bridge over the Mersey (*Field*, 7 July 1951).

The jackdaw (*Corvus mouldula*) has become a regular chimney-pot nester, especially on the west coast of Ireland where the chough (*Pyrrhocorax*) occupies the sea cliffs. In Cornwall the reverse is the case. The small Kensington Gardens colony, which formerly nested in the Church Street rookery, breed regularly in tree-holes opposite Barkers' Stores, or did so until 1940.

The jackdaw has bred regularly in several European and Asiatic towns even though suitable tree accommodation was available.

The house crow of India (*C. splendens*) has formed a close association with man, breeding in the centre of many large cities; its outlying colonies at Aden, Port Sudan and Zanzibar stick rigidly to gardens within built-up districts.

In India have occurred cases where crows have used nothing but old pieces of wire for nest building and in one case an entire nest was built of spectacle frames stolen from Laurence & Mayo in Simla (*Field*, 29 May 1958).

The magpie (*Pica*) has bred in inner London and has become a town bird in Stockholm and in Iraq. In Lapland they are largely scavengers round villages and Lapp encampments.

Magpies are particularly fond of playing round religious buildings. In Ushant the church was a regular playground soon after dawn, the whole island population collecting for the fun of gambolling among gargoyles and angels. I have seen similar games in Stockholm and Arctic Lapland and on mosques in Iraq. This is all the more remarkable as nowhere in its range is the magpie a cliff bird.

The magpie was a common bird in north-east France during the First World War, breeding in roadside trees. After the war in 1919, with all the trees gone, he took to nesting on telegraph poles.

The jay (*Garrulus*) has now established himself in inner London and it is no uncommon sight to see them playing among chimney-pots and on the Natural History Museum.

The Siberian jay (*Cractes*) is increasingly becoming dependent on man; in winter in Arctic Lapland they can always be found scavenging round Lapp encampments and even in summer I have seen them in cottage gardens.

A pair of full-winged red-billed chough (*Pyrrhocorax*) bred at the base of a chimney-pot at my old home—Mottisfont Abbey—and laid eggs which were always robbed by a tame raven. The same chough bred on the house at Lilford.

In Switzerland the Alpine chough (*P. alpinus*) is increasingly nesting in buildings and on bridges.

Starlings (*Sturnus*) frequently make use of buildings for nesting. In some of the West Irish islands, where suitable trees do not exist, they are exclusively chimney-pot nesters. Communal roosts on buildings occur in London. My first note of starling roosts in London goes back to 1891 when about two hundred birds were roosting on the Serpentine island in December alongside about twenty-five woodpigeons; this continued until at least 1897 when a few began to collect on the National Gallery—perhaps fifty individuals; many still roosted on the Serpentine island up to 1910 and by then the National Gallery roost was huge, many hundreds of birds. By 1914 this roost had spread to Charing Cross Station and a few on St Martin's Church. In the winter 1940–1 the National Gallery roost was almost deserted and the Charing Cross roost much increased.

This is at variance with the dates given by Nicholson in *Birds and Man*, where starling roosts in London are believed to have commenced between 1910 and 1920.

Throughout their range from West Ireland to Turkestan and Mosul in Iraq, starlings prefer human habitations to holes in trees for nesting; and of all British birds they show a preference for buildings as song-posts.

In South West Africa, on a four-mile stretch of railway south of Windhoek, almost every telegraph pole had a large twig-nest among the insulators; the nests were unoccupied; a railway official told me they were a great nuisance and as fast as the nests were pulled down they were rebuilt; he thought the bird was some sort of starling.

The house sparrow (*Passer domesticus*) in Britain depends largely on man for nesting sites, shelter and food. In the days of horse-drawn vehicles it was no uncommon sight to see hundreds in the Strand and Piccadilly. Every scrap of horse-dung was hurriedly removed by municipal scavengers but the sparrows were always first on to it. The house sparrow forms enormous communal roosts, the largest known, many thousands, being in Lisbon. Enormous roosts have also been recorded in Cairo and neighbourhood (Moreau, *Ibis*, 1931, p. 204). The removal of the horse from London has reduced the house sparrow to quite small numbers. Both the house sparrow and the tree sparrow (*P. montana*) depend largely on grain. Neither species was in Siberia before Russian colonisation and grain-growing (Goeldt, 1914). Both species are now common wherever humans occur. The rapid spread of the house sparrow in New Zealand and America has been strictly conditioned by man. But there still exist sparrow populations not dependent on man. In Afghanistan and Baluchistan they breed freely in earth banks far removed from man and man's cultivation; the tree sparrow is the house bird, nesting in houses and forming large communal roosts in winter on creepers up against a house, when the house sparrow has migrated to warmer climes. In parts of Arabia the house sparrow breeds hundreds of miles from buildings or farmland and has become a bush bird, or rather has remained a bush bird, which was almost certainly his original niche. In Lapland the house sparrow is entirely dependent on man. In Java, where the European sparrow was introduced, they only occur near the dwellings of Europeans (*Fürst. Natw. Wschr.*, x, p. 558).

In India the weaver (*Ploceus philippinus*) often places its nest on telegraph wires as a protection against predatory monkeys, and there are cases on record of sunbirds using similar sites.

The long-tailed broadbill (*Psarisomus dalhousiae*) is also known to hang its nests from electric wires spanning a nullah near Mussoorie (*Journ. Bomb. N.H. Soc.*, 1952, p. 271).

The bunting (*Emberiza striolata*) is a bird of rocky hill slopes almost throughout its range from India to North Africa, though I have found them nesting in ruined buildings in Rajputana. But in north-west Africa they have become a house bird, almost an inside-the-house bird, which makes the obtaining of specimens extremely difficult and always needing the consent of the owner of the house.

In Greenland the snow bunting (*Plectrophenax*) is a house bird, often nesting in the busiest parts of settlements.

The rock pipit (*Anthus spinoletta*) breeds regularly in walls and houses in West Greenland; and in Alderney I found a nest in the verandah of a ruined cottage.

In Britain and in many parts of the continent the wagtail (*Motacilla alba*) has become a house and farm-yard bird; and the grey wagtail (*M. cinerea*) often resorts in winter to farm-yards. Nicholson records them at the courtyard fountain in the Naval and Military Club in Piccadilly.

Joseph George (*Journ. Bombay N.H. Soc.*, Dec. 1957, p. 943) records a purple sunbird (*Nectarinia asiatica*) nesting on the pull-cord of a lavatory cistern in a bathroom in Dehra Dun and successfully hatching young.

Both the blue and great tits often breed in houses, the former two years running in my London house, after which they have taken up residence in a nesting-box.

The wall-creeper (*Tichodroma*) does not distinguish between cliffs and buildings. I have seen them running up the Kutb Minar near Delhi, on monasteries in Ladak and on houses in Pindi and Peshawar. At our hotel at Gavarnie in the Pyrenees a bird appeared one morning at our bedroom window.

In *The Times* of 9 May 1951 is a record of a blackbird (*Turdus merula*) nesting on a ninth-storey roof garden in Baker Street; and in the *Field* (13 March 1958) is the record of a nest on a railway wagon in Yorkshire, four chicks being hatched. The ring ouzel (*Turdus torquatus*) has bred in inhabited houses in Inverness-shire and elsewhere in Scotland (*Brit. B.*, 1952, p. 416).

The wheatear (*Oenanthe*) is known to breed in inhabited houses in both Greenland and Iceland; and in Westmorland they have been known to breed under the sleepers of railway lines and in railway ballast (*Brit. B.*, 1952, p. 468).

The chat (*Oenanthe leucopyga*), usually a bird of desolate ravines and rocky slopes, has, at Siwa Oasis, developed urban habits, never wandering away from houses and breeding in houses, and has developed a tameness which enables them to sit on baskets of dates in crowded market-places.

The black redstart (*Phoenicurus ochruros*) was attracted to London by bombed areas which supplied ample breeding sites, but the tidying-up has reduced their numbers. In Holland birds ceased to be attracted to ruined cities as soon as rebuilding commenced.

In Britain and some parts of Holland the robin (*Erithacus*) has learned friendship with the gardener and it is a most remarkable fact that throughout the British Isles, even in remote hills where the robin can seldom meet a human, he has become almost fearless, apparently conscious of his association with Christmas and the warm place he holds in the hearts of the British. This is in marked contrast to the robin of most of the Continent, where he is a shy skulker and seldom seen in a garden. The robin is always attracted to up-turned earth, hence his companionship with the grave-digger, a habit which may have stimulated his association with humans and man's sentimentality towards himself.

Man's affection for the robin is misplaced sentiment. His attendance on man, whether it be grave-digger, gardener or old lady, is based on stomach-love—grubs and small worms. The robin's character does not deserve our affection; he is the vilest of aggressors, greedy, selfish and vicious. He flaunts his vulgar red waistcoat in the face of competition and his behaviour at the bird table is that of a spiv or teddy-boy in a fashionable restaurant. His stomach dominates his life in unashamed greed and selfishness—a vulgar little bounder.

Both wren (*Troglodytes*) and dipper (*Cinclus*) will breed on buildings and under bridges not only in the British Isles but also in the Himalayas. At a house in Scotland a wren would always enter my window soon after dawn, conduct a systematic search round the room, inspect the windows for insects and then quietly remove himself. If his particular window was not open, he would flutter up against it until I opened it for him. This technique continued for four consecutive years. The wren had been known to nest on the curtain rail of a dining-room and successfully bring off her brood.

The *Illustrated London News* of 26 July 1952 records a wren building its nest under the running-board of a lorry and undertaking many journeys from Swanley in Kent to Covent Garden and back twice a week with both eggs and chicks.

A rather similar case is recorded (*Bokmakierie*, 1952, p. 15) of a pair of mountain chats (*Oenanthe montana*) nesting under a railway coach at Vredefort, O.F.S., and rearing their chicks in spite of the wagon travelling sixty-two miles every day from 10.10 a.m. to 5.10 p.m.

Were the swallow (*Hirundo*) and house martin (*Delichon*) as abundant in Europe before the advent of man and his buildings? If so, where did they nest? They have probably been associated with man since the latter was a cave-dweller; in fact they probably used the caves before the advent of man. Today, the swallow is almost entirely dependent on man for nesting sites, as is the house martin; but occasionally the former has been found nesting in caves and the latter on both sea and inland cliffs. In Wiltshire I found a very beautiful nest of a house martin in a chalk pit and largely constructed of white chalk-mud; it was overhung by a brilliant blue *Polygala* which enhanced its charm. In the Himalayas the house martin breeds entirely on cliffs, rarely in houses and in Siberia entirely in houses, which must be a very recent choice, if indeed it bred in northern Siberia at all before the advent of man and his houses.

Baxter and Rintoul (*B. Scotland*, 1, p. 237) ascribe the decrease of house martins in towns and villages in Scotland to lack of mud due to tarmac roads. I think it is more likely due to the persecution of nesting birds by persons troubled by twittering and that delightful subdued song. In St Andrews and in Caithness I have seen men with ladders tearing down nests full of young and throwing them into the garden because owners were disturbed in the early hours.

In tropical Africa the races of the European swallow are rapidly abandoning cliff and cave building and are now using houses. When I first went to Kenya in 1901 I was stationed at Fort Hall and Nyeri where there were no houses and where several species of swallow bred locally on river banks and earth cliffs; they have now, in the majority of cases, transferred their nests to buildings. This refers more particularly to the forms *arcticincta*, *aethiopica*, *senegalensis* and *emini*.

Van Someren (*Novit. Zoolog.*, 1922, p. 92) lists the East African swallows, which breed in houses, in earth banks or on cliffs. In 1900 there was scarcely a house in Kenya up-country; the colony is now almost urbanised and it would be interesting to ascertain if swallows are abandoning natural nesting sites for human habitations.

The red-rumped swallow (*H. rufula*) in Baluchistan breeds exclusively on horizontal rock faces, though buildings are available. But in Kenya they have taken to buildings though rock faces are available. They now breed in houses in both Syria and British Somaliland.

The sand martin (*Riparia riparia*) almost always nests in earth or sand tunnels but has occasionally bred in holes in brickwork and drain-pipes. In Egypt I have seen a colony of the local race (*shelleyi*) nesting partly in tunnels on flat sand, partly under an old concrete floor and partly in crevices in old masonry. The crag martin (*R. rupestris* and races) nests both on cliffs and in buildings. The *paludicolor* and *cincta* groups excavate their own holes, as does *riparia*. The *fuligula* group builds half-cup nests of mud in caves, on cliffs or in houses.

The swifts (*Apus apus* and *A. melba*) breed both in buildings and in natural crevices. The European swift breeds abundantly in many large cities, including London, and is particularly common in central Paris. There is a large colony at Hammersmith. In Jerusalem both common and Alpine swift breed commonly in the old city. In Kenya there is a huge colony of several species of swift near Naivasha, all nesting in natural rock. Before 1900 there was not a house outside Mombasa where swifts could nest, but as houses and bridges have been built the small white-rumped swift (*A. affinis*) has rapidly changed from a rock- to a building-nester. In Arabia and India the species breeds in both rock and buildings; in Morocco almost exclusively in buildings though many good rock sites are available; in South Africa exclusively in buildings so far as I know. At Mogadischu in Italian Somaliland there is a colony of several thousand pairs nesting on the cathedral—probably the world's largest swiftery.

The needle-tailed swifts (*Chaetura*) breed in rock crevices, holes in trees and occasionally in buildings; the largest I have seen was in Mussoorie (Himalayas), where many pairs were nesting under eaves in the middle of the town. Sick (*Journ. f. Orn.*, 1951, p. 38) records *Chaetura andrei*, which normally nests in hollow palms, as nesting in chimneys in several Brazilian towns.

Though usually nesting in tree-holes, the hoopoe (*Upupa*) frequently breeds in old masonry in Egypt and India; in the former country, the species has become almost a house bird, very tame, and will 'drum' within a few feet of man. At Thebes in Lower Egypt they have bred in holes near coloured mural paintings.

All rollers (*Coracias*) will occasionally breed in old buildings, especially in Iraq, but I have no record of bee-eaters (*Merops*) doing so.

Hindwood (*Emu*, 1947, p. 117) records the kookaburra (*Dacelo gigas*) nesting in a hole in the wall in the centre of Sydney.

Considerable damage to church spires has been done in East Anglia by the green woodpecker (*Picus viridis*), as many as twenty churches having had to expend considerable sums of money in consequence; the attacks are usually made in March, 'birds drumming furiously on spires, puncturing the outer shingles with holes about the size of a sixpence and sometimes as large as a cricket ball' (*The Times*, 14 Feb. 1955). During an influx of great spotted woodpeckers (*Dendrocopos major*) to the Isle of May (Scotland), where trees do not exist, they were seen running up the lighthouse, the nearest approach to a tree on the island.

Considerable damage to telegraph poles has been done in both Britain and India by woodpeckers, possibly attracted by the humming of the wires.

A cuckoo (*Cuculus canorus*) has been known to deposit its egg in a wagtail's nest inside a building (*Brit. B.*, 1952, p. 417).

Surprisingly few owls have an association with man. Of the eagle owls (*Bubo bubo*), only the desert races make use of man and then to a limited extent. *Bubo b. desertorum* has on several occasions taken up residence down wells in Egypt and the Sudan, but their normal habitat is among boulders and in caves. The little owls (*Athene noctua* and *brama*) often breed in buildings. The European scops (*Otus scops*) and other members of the genus occasionally breed in old buildings but in Crete the scops invariably breeds in inhabited buildings. On one occasion, on the slopes of Mount Ida a female was brooding eggs within four feet of my bed on the verandah, and the male, at dusk, would perch and hoot on a pole of my mosquito net, scarcely troubling to move when I shouted at him. The barn owl (*Tyto*) usually nests in buildings when available, in Britain almost always; and I have never found them away from buildings either in Egypt or Arabia. Church belfries infested with bats are often used by white owls, when they pay no attention to the penetrating vibrations of continuous bell-ringing. At a temporary office I had in Haifa a pair spent all day, erect and stupid, within a foot or so of my only window in full view of my desk. Opening and shutting the window did not bother them beyond producing a hiss, and many times during somewhat heated conversations they would introduce humour by weird noises, when tempers would be reduced to normal.

The brown owl (*Strix aluco*) has become a London bird and breeds now in the Temple Gardens and in all the large parks. In 1941 on frosty nights when on Home Guard duties at Admiralty Arch and in Trafalgar Square, I would often hear them hoot, once apparently from the Nelson Column whence I saw an owl fly towards Charing Cross, no doubt to raid the huge starling roost which must be a permanent source of food for the St James's Park owls.

In 1896 peregrines (*Falco peregrinus*) bred on Salisbury Cathedral; one of the chicks, a tiercel, lived to be adult, but was so nervous that we could not train him; a second chick was trained by Gerald Lascelles and was still alive in 1901. In Caithness a pair bred on the ruined Sinclair Castle near Wick in 1927; and in 1924 they bred successfully on Cologne Cathedral.

The American peregrine (*P. f. anatum*) has been reported breeding in the business centre of Philadelphia (*Auk*, 1947, p. 312). Other cases have been reported of them breeding on a bridge, on a Canadian sky-scraper and on an hotel in New York City.

Wintering Barbary falcons (*F. p. pelegrinoides*) make full use of large

PLATE 42

Red Kite in Old London

public buildings in Khartoum, sleeping by day and hunting morning and evening; and wintering *F. p. peregrinus* does likewise in Khartoum.

The lanner (*biarmicus*) breeds regularly on the Great Pyramid and *Falco concolor* in the Old Fort at Mombasa in 1901 and again in 1914. On Mogador Island in Morocco Eleonora's falcon breeds in some numbers on both sea-cliffs and ruined buildings.

The lesser kestrel (*F. naumanni*) freely nests in buildings, the largest colony I have seen comprising about fifty pair in the old castle at Acre; and in Spain they favour cathedrals.

The common kestrel often nests in ruined buildings and in London they have nested on the Nelson Column in Trafalgar Square. In 1952 a pair of kestrel reared their young on the Thames side of the Savoy Hotel in London. In Palestine as many as fifteen nests were found among ruins in the Judaean Highlands. In Egypt, where buildings are favourable for nesting, they prefer palm trees.

I have only once come across a communal roost of kestrel. It was in October in Ross-shire when at sundown about fifteen birds would come in from all directions and sit about the roof, usually on the south side and in shelter. I presumed they were migrants, for the roost commenced in early October and ceased suddenly in mid-November. By day they would scatter in all directions and it was an exception to see a bird on the estate.

The black kite (*Milvus migrans*) has become a city bird in the East, breeding on buildings both in Cairo and Bombay often overlooking crowded streets.

Which kite was so abundant in old London during the sixteenth century? It has always been assumed that it was the red kite which then nested commonly in Britain. But the red kite is not and never has been a proletarian, assuming the role of the sanitary squad, whilst the black kite has from time immemorial and still is the scavenger of cities. Clusius in 1571 thought there were as many kites in London as in Cairo and surely he would have noted the difference between the two species; the Cairo kite is and always has been the black kite, and I believe the kite of old London was *Milvus migrans*.

But there is strong evidence that the London kite was in fact the red kite. Fitter (*London's Birds*, p. 102) quotes Turner, who in 1544 wrote:

I know two sorts of kites, the greater and the less; the greater is in colour nearly rufous, and in England is abundant and remarkably rapacious. This kind is wont to snatch food out of children's hands, in our cities and towns. The other kind is smaller, blacker, and more rarely haunts cities. This I do not remember to have seen in England, though in Germany most frequently. (*Turner on Birds*, ed. H. A. Evans, Cambridge 1903, p. 117.)

The Egyptian vulture (*Neophron*) used to nest freely in Cairo. In the Pyrenees and Spain they nest on cliffs only, but in many parts of India they have joined the proletarian ranks and breed in crowded towns.

In days gone by the osprey (*Pandion*) frequently nested on ruined buildings in Scotland, and still does so elsewhere.

The white stork (*Ciconia*) is closely associated with man. There is much competition in northern Europe and elsewhere to enjoy the honour of a nest on one's premises; this association has gone so far as to induce farmers to erect nesting platforms and actually build the nest for these desirable birds. Surely such pampering cannot be good for a species?

The white stork, which has recently bred regularly in South Africa, has retained his preference for proximity to human dwellings; whereas the black stork, also recently breeding in South Africa, retains his preference for forests.

Wildfowl soon learn to take advantage of the protection afforded by man in built-up areas. Whooper swan (*Cygnus cygnus*) have wintered at Carlisle on the Eden and become very tame, taking food thrown to them. Tufted duck have established themselves on London's lakes. A male scaup (*A. marila*) accepted the hospitality of London for many years and most British duck have from time to time spent a few days' immunity from man amidst man's densest population. But the most amazing and unique sight is the congregation of wild duck of several species which spend the day on the tea-garden pond at Giza Zoological Gardens; arriving about dawn and moving out about sunset, they doze and rest and preen all day long within a few feet of chattering tea-parties; both teal and pintail will scramble for crumbs, whilst I have seen wild gadwall asleep and only woken by a prod from an umbrella. And these same birds assume their customary wildness so soon as they leave their daylight sanctuary. One afternoon during the First World War an officer cracked a whip near the pond; up and off went the whole duck population. That officer incurred a severe reprimand from the Garden staff.

The woodpigeon (*Columba palumbus*) has become a garden bird in Iraq and a town bird in London, where I have encouraged a bird to take food from the hand. They have also bred with success on my London house at the foot of a chimney-pot. The male would sit in April on the chimney and from my bed I could hear the eerie coo come drifting down the chimney at dawn. There are many other records of woodpigeon breeding in houses and barns. One of the wildest birds where persecuted, they have lost their fear of man in London where, I regret, they are now on the black list. Surely the pleasure the Londoner gets from this beautiful bird far outweighs his depredations on a few unhealthy peas and beans in allotments. My London garden is the only place where I have seen woodpigeon coming freely to a bird table.

The rock pigeons of London present a most interesting case of double adaptation and evolution in reverse; also an example of autolycism. Descended from a stock which nests in the wildest places and which rank among the wildest birds, they have been degraded by artificial selection into monstrous varieties bearing little outward resemblance to their ancestors and have, in London, completely lost their wildness. London is regarded as one huge conglomeration of caves and cliffs, there are unlimited breeding sites in buildings and under the Thames bridges, and unlimited food is provided by a bird-loving litter-strewing public. The London population of rock pigeon is slowly returning to the original type, a process retarded by a constant intake of domestic breeds. But the wild type was gaining ground until 1952. In 1920 about 7 per cent of Trafalgar Square birds were pure *Columba livia*. Since then the percentage has steadily risen and in 1938 was 15 per cent. In 1944 it had dropped to 11 per cent and it stands today (1958) at only 5 per cent. During recent years I have noted a marked tendency to melanism among London's feral pigeons not only in Trafalgar Square but also at the Natural History Museum in South Kensington. In May 1950 about 10 per cent were melanics, and in May 1952 about 47 per cent were melanics. Is this another example of industrial melanism? In a wild state the rock pigeon, though usually breeding in coastal caves, also breeds in ruined buildings in Scotland and India, and down wells in the latter country and almost throughout the East.

The dove (*S. decaocto*) has recently made a spectacular extension of range from south-east Europe to Holland and Scandinavia. This dove is usually attached to human settlement and it has been suggested that human factors have assisted the extension; but if that were so, why did not the extension take place centuries ago when conditions were equally favourable?

Many species of dove (*Streptopelia*) have taken to nesting in verandahs in hot climates.

The cormorant (*Phalacrocorax carbo*) is no respecter of buildings, which he uses as a place where he can dry his wings and as a latrine. In 1910 I saw hundreds lined up on the roof of the Sultan's Palace in Constantinople, fouling the whole building. By the Sultan's orders a fire engine was in constant attendance to scare them off but it was found that the extreme top of the roof could not be reached; and the little spray which did reach them was much appreciated by the birds.

A cormorant has been photographed on the cross of St Paul's Cathedral and Jouanin (*Oiseau*, 1951, pp. 71-3) records twenty-seven cormorants on the Panthéon and Notre-Dame in Paris in January, remaining a fortnight.

Pelicans will sit on buildings and ships on the Californian coast and at Port Sudan I have seen dozens balancing themselves in a high wind on wireless masts and cables. On the South American Pacific coast they are a common harbour scavenger, sitting on small craft and jetties.

The fulmar (*Fulmarus*) has been known to breed on ruined buildings. I came across it at the ruins of Sinclair Castle near Wick where two pair had nests within a few yards of a peregrine falcon in 1927.

Stormy petrels (*Hydrobates pelagicus*) breed not only in stone walls, but on a small island off Alderney they breed on the rafters under the eaves of a cottage.

The Senegal stone-curlew (*Burhinus senegalensis*) of the Egyptian Delta has solved the problem of breeding under desert conditions in a highly cultivated part of the world by nesting on the flat roofs of dwellings. As many as twenty-one nests with eggs have been seen on a single roof at the Delta Barrage and at least a dozen pair used to nest on the lion house in the Giza Zoological Gardens. Many bred in central Cairo on the Kasr-el-Nil Barracks.

Witherby has recorded black guillemots (*Uria grylla*) breeding on an old harbour wall.

On Steep Holme Island in the Bristol Channel I found herring gulls (*Larus argentatus*) and the British lesser black-backed gull breeding up against the old monastery walls which were none the less inhabited by my friend Harry Cox and his goats (1932). So tame were the brooding gulls that we could pass within touching distance of them and when a goat approached the nest it was met by nothing more than an angry open mouth displaying the brilliant inside coloration. It has been recorded that a pair of herring gulls persistently nested in a basket in a fishing-boat in Cornwall. There are also many records of herring gulls breeding on houses in Dover, in the west of England and in Ireland.

Kittiwakes have nested for years on the window-ledges of a store in Dunbar and at Aalesund in Norway buildings round the harbour are plastered with kittiwakes' nests.

I believe the platform of Hawes Junction railway station in Yorkshire to be the only platform in the British Isles where grouse resort in hard weather, and on at least two occasions they have remained on the platform with trains in the station.

The red-legged partridge (*Alectoris*) has used a haystack in which to place its nest some five feet from the ground.

J. K. Stanford (*Field*, August 7, 1958) records this partridge nesting on a ledge of an inhabited house twenty feet from the ground and near the front door.

In the north Arabian desert, some hundred miles east of Amman, I came across a flat-roofed ruined building standing alone on flat desert but with a few grass-clad wadis near by; I lunched there and was surprised to find a pair of see-see (*Ammoperdix*) had taken up residence on the roof. This bird inhabits desolate rocky wadis and is seldom seen away from hills or cliffs of some sort. But here was a pair well over sixty miles from their usual habitat and treating a ruined house as a kopje. They must have had a long exploratory run before finding such a refuge. Without cover of any sort they would be at the complete mercy of predatory birds; this serves to illustrate the immunity of desert birds from predators.

Moreau (*Ibis*, 1942, pp. 254-6) gives many examples of birds making use of man in Africa.

One of the most remarkable examples of birds taking advantage of man's indiscretions occurred after the First World War. North-east France became a devastated area, almost treeless, and quickly reverted to unfenced common land. In 1919, when I toured this devastated area for a week, I found the little bustard (*Tetrax*) by no means uncommon, every evening two or three pairs being seen doing their evening butterfly flight. But by the autumn of 1920 re-fencing, re-planting and cultivation had de-commonised the land and I believe no bustards came in 1921.

The above cases comprise those more notable examples of birds taking advantage of man, especially those which I have personally come across. There are of course innumerable other cases—thrushes nesting in wheelbarrows, robins in flower-pots, blue tits down drain-pipes, wheatears and sand-martins in haystacks, and of course the use made by many species of nesting boxes.

Association with ships

The scavenging habit of gulls, terns and skuas around ships in harbour and at sea is too well known to describe. The only gull I have never seen around ships either in harbour or at sea is the slender-billed gull (*genei*). *Ridibundus, hemprichii* and *leucopthalmus* will seldom follow a ship at sea out of sight of land.

In June 1955, when travelling from Harwich to Denmark, I noticed that many black-headed gulls followed the ship for about three hours (60 miles) and then settled on the sea towards dusk. And early on the following day when 60 miles from Esbjerg we picked up large numbers of herring and black-backed gulls who accompanied the ship into Esbjerg. I spoke to the ship's captain about it and he told me that from both Esbjerg and Harwich gulls follow the ship for about 60 miles and then remain on the water until the next ship passes and this is accompanied back to harbour.

The great skua (*Stercorarius skua*) will follow ships for long distances—once from Iceland to the Shetland Isles and again for two days in the Bay of Biscay—but I have never seen the smaller skuas follow ships except for very short distances.

Most of the petrels will attend ships for food, especially fishing craft. It has been suggested that the recent spread of the fulmar is due to modern trawling; but the basic reason is, I believe, the spread of the herring during the past 300 years from Norwegian to British waters. This excellent fish used to be known as the Norwegian herring and was quite unknown in the North Sea and off the west Scottish coast.

Gannets have often been seen to take food thrown from ships and they have also been known to feed on fish thrown to them in harbours.

Just north of Perim at the south end of the Red Sea on 1 January 1951, many gannets (*leucogaster* and *melanops*) came into view, some of them flying level with the ship at wave height and endeavouring to catch the flying fish disturbed by the bows of the ship; there were many attempts but I only witnessed a single capture, when the fish was caught while it planed over the surface. Birds were cruising at about 16 knots with a 12-m.p.h. head wind and some forty yards from the ship. Only about a dozen birds, out of many hundred, were practising this sport. Doubtless it will extend and become popular if it proves successful.

The huge and varied collection of scavenging sea birds which attend whaling fleets is well known and I have nothing to add to published data on the subject.

The use of ships by birds for long-distance voyages is a much neglected cause of straggling, which has so often been attributed by enthusiasts to the theory of 'drift.'

The following cases of assisted passages have come to my notice.

Corvus splendens. Malcolm Davis (*Auk*, 1951, p. 529) describes how four crows came aboard his ship off Colombo and remained for six days, eventually flying off to Cape Guardafui in Somaliland. This type of transportion might well account for colonies of this crow at Zanzibar, Aden and Port Sudan.

Sturnus vulgaris. Peter Scott, during a journey from Europe to Venezuela, observed starlings aboard and these only left the ship when in sight of Venezuela. Eberhard Jany (*Vogelwarte*, 1957, p. 140) records a single starling coming aboard a steamer on 10 December mid-way between Colombo and Aden and remaining on board until opposite Socotra, when it flew off.

MacArthur and Klopfer (*Brit. B.*, 1958, p. 358) record four small American Passerines being carried in September by ship from New York for three days towards Britain, two *Zonotrichia albicollis* not leaving the ship until the British Islands were sighted.

When I was travelling by Shell tanker from Liverpool to the Persian Gulf, a small flock of bramblings (*Fringilla montifringilla*) came aboard off Ushant when in sight of land and remained on board until we reached Port Said, from 21 to 28 December 1950. They were fed and watered regularly on board. They are a rare winter visitor to Egypt. Should these 'assisted passage' records be accepted?

Motacilla. W. W. A. Phillips (*Ibis*, 1952, p. 530) records that on 10 April 1951 a yellow wagtail came aboard a ship off Alexandria and was seen daily until 20 April when the ship was but 900 miles from Boston. It fed on flies near cages of monkeys.

Malcolm Davies (*op. cit.*) records two white wagtails coming aboard at the south end of the Red Sea and only leaving the ship at Port Said.

Michael Jeneid (*epist.*) records a great grey shrike boarding his ship at Kronstadt in the Baltic and remaining on board until off the Norfolk coast, when it left the ship and—probably the same bird—was trapped by his mother in a Heligoland-type trap only a quarter of an hour later.

Erithacus rubecula. In *Bird Notes*, XXVI, 4, 1955, p. 105, is recorded the case of a robin coming aboard off Ushant and remaining on board until the ship docked in London. It had travelled 400 miles in reversed migration and had accepted food on board.

Turdus sp. G. M. Tait of Oporto records that when he was returning from Canada in October 1929 twelve brown thrush-like birds flew aboard off Newfoundland and only left the ship when in sight of Ireland.

Merops superciliosus persicus. When I was returning from India in 1900 three bee-eaters came aboard in the Suez Canal on 21 May, only leaving the ship on 25 May, when in the Straits of Bonifacio. The ship was filthy dirty, buzzing with flies and noxious insects, which suited the birds.

Upupa epops. Malcolm Davis (*op. cit.*) records a hoopoe boarding his ship in the Gulf of Aden on 19 November and only leaving at Suez. I also have a record of a hoopoe remaining on board from India (28 February) to Gibraltar (17 March).

Nyctea. In 1895 we received an adult snowy owl from my uncle Robert Holt of Liverpool; it had come aboard one of his ships in October when near Halifax, Nova Scotia, and remained on board until Ireland was sighted, when the bird was caught up. It had travelled right across the North Atlantic. It lived at Mottisfont until 1900.

Falco candicans. Major Dorrien Smith of Tresco (Isles of Scilly) recounted to me that his sister, returning from America in the autumn of 1921, observed a Greenland falcon come aboard when off Nova Scotia. The bird remained on the ship until the Bishop's Light (Isles of Scilly) was sighted, when the falcon flew off. On that same day a Greenland falcon arrived at Tresco and remained the whole winter.

Falco peregrinus. The late Capt. F. Guest, returning from Canada in October 1920, observed a peregrine on his ship when off Newfoundland. The bird remained for three days, a passage of about 1,200 miles, when it was caught and killed by one of the crew. I have the specimen in my collection, an adult male of the American race. Again, W. Byers (*Auk*, 1957, p. 265) records that on 3 November 1953, when about 600 miles north of Honolulu and 500 miles from the nearest land, a peregrine came aboard at 8 a.m. The bird was last seen on 10 November when 700 miles from Japan. The bird had remained on the ship for nearly 3,500 miles and had been seen to catch and eat both terns and petrels.

Ajaia ajaja. Van Tyne (*Wilson Bull.*, 1943, p. 127) records three roseate spoonbills boarding a ship on 18 January 1943 in the Florida Straits at 7 a.m. and remaining on board till 5 p.m.

Butorides striatus. Capt. Marcuse, returning from America in 1921, observed a little green heron in the rigging when in long. 75° N. off the Bahamas. The bird remained on board until the ship was north of the Azores, long. 30° W. by lat. 40° N. The bird came aboard on 23 September and was caught and killed on 1 October. I have the specimen in my collection.

The record of this bird being taken in Cornwall in October 1889 should be accepted. It was shot on the fringe of a small pond at Penrice near St Austell by the keeper of Sir C. Sawle, who described this wanton act to me in 1896 when I saw the bird stuffed in the house. I took the specimen to the British Museum, where it was identified by Mr Bowdler Sharpe. The specimen was exhibited at the Linnaean Society in April 1890 (see *Zoologist*, 1890, pp. 105 and 181).

Michael Jeneid (*epist.*) records a dotterel and a lanner falcon carried on his ship from off Malta to Port Said.

Porzana porzana. Voous (*Ardea*, 1957, p. 89) records a specimen of the spotted crake from the Lesser Antilles. It was caught alive on 8 October 1956. This must surely be an assisted passage.

When I was travelling from Aden to Bombay in January 1901 four spotted crake came aboard on the 25th and remained aboard until we reached Bombay on the 29th.

I also have many records of short-distance assisted passages varying from 30-40 miles to about 100 miles. I do not believe it possible for an American Passerine, unaccustomed to long-distance flight, to cross the Atlantic without making use of ships.

A remarkable case came to my notice at Dongola in the Sudan. Two pairs of house-sparrows (*Passer domesticus*) had built their nests in the furled sail of the Governor's launch. We took the launch up-stream on two successive days for fifteen and twenty miles respectively. At first the sparrows evinced great excitement but they accompanied the launch the whole day, frequently flying ashore for food and water, and on the second day they repeated the trip without any signs of distress. They had travelled seventy miles in two days with their nurseries.

A rather similar case occurred many years ago near Maidenhead when a pair of pied wagtails built their nest in the furled awning of a motor launch, laid their eggs and hatched their young, despite the boat being used every week-end for long trips up and down the river. The birds always accompanied the launch and were sometimes absent from Maidenhead from after breakfast until evening.

Luiking (*Limosa*, 1954, p. 118) records a pair of swallows (*Hirundo tahitica javanica*) nesting on a coastal tanker which made daily local sailings. They even accompanied the ship to Singapore for docking.

There have been many cases of European swallows obtaining assisted passages over the Alps in aeroplanes when on autumn migration in unfavourable weather.

Birds making use of trains

A habit, only acquired during the last thirty years in India, is the attendance of mynahs (*Acridotheres*) on trains at stations; they scavenge under the carriages, in the carriages, and among the seething mass of screaming passengers; many get caught in carriages when the train moves and the doors are shut, and get assisted passages to the next station.

BIRDS MAKING USE OF MAN FOR FOOD

General

THIS is an enormous subject, including the raiding of crops and gardens, bird tables, the wholesale feeding of birds such as takes place in St James's Park, the attendance of birds on ships, at slaughter-houses, the opening of milk bottles by tits, attending man when shooting, not only for wounded birds but for disturbed prey, following the plough, the habits of *Indicator* the honey-guide, etc. Many of these have been adequately dealt with by Nicholson in *Birds and Man*. I shall not attempt a survey of crop-raiding and garden fruit-raiding, both of which are universal and outside my competence. Neither shall I deal with bird tables or the wholesale feeding of birds —a rather disgusting orgy of gluttony and greed. But an interesting extension of this came to my notice on Snowdon recently. Hundreds of trippers ascend the mountain, lunching on their way up and distributing their litter and remains of food. Both the black-headed and common gull go up with the trippers and no sooner does a party sit down for lunch than the gulls also sit down near them and of course get fed.

There is one aspect of the nature of the British countryside which affects bird populations. The noticeable abundance of smaller Passerines in Britain is not so much due to our national love of birds and a degree of protection they enjoy but to the fact that since the day of enclosures the advent of hedges has afforded them shelter and breeding sites which they enjoy in no other country in the world and this is entirely due to human progress. The great variety of our countryside, ponds, hedgerows, small coppices, common land, park land, etc., is a tremendous attraction to most of the smaller Passerines in contra-distinction to the large forests and unfenced open spaces of the Continent. Of course, in those countries inhabited by Latin races where robins' tongues, nightingales' tongues and other forms of *beccafico* are enjoyed, the scarcity of birds is due to quite other causes.

The probable reason why the crested lark has never established itself in Britain is the intense cultivation and lack of waste land; it is human agency which keeps them out.

Slaughter-houses

It is only natural that flesh-eating birds should congregate round slaughter-houses. Except *Gyps fulvus* and *G. rüppelli*, all the African vultures come to slaughter-houses; the most usual are *Neophron*, *Necrosyrtes* and the black kite (*Milvus migrans*). The slaughter-houses at Port Sudan support over 400 *Neophron*, many *Necrosyrtes* and hundreds of black kite. The tawny eagles (*rapax* and *nipalensis*) come freely to slaughter-houses but not the other eagles nor any buzzard.

The lammergeier (*Gypaëtos*) is a rare visitor to slaughter-houses though an odd one may be seen at Quetta and Kabul. But at Quetta (1913–14) this fine bird has developed a habit amounting to commensalism. They hang about the soldiers' barrack-rooms and accept bones thrown to them; I have seen as many as seven sharing dinners with British soldiers. On one occasion a puppy, also scavenging, was seized and carried off by a lammergeier—the only occasion on which I have seen this bird take a living thing. The lammergeier is quite unable to deal with a dead horse or ox, the skin being too tough. He has to wait until it has been opened by vultures before he can get at his favourite food—bones.

187

The marabou stork (*Leptoptilos*) in Africa is a pure vulture in habit, soaring with them and feeding with them on carcases, often at slaughter-houses. In India, especially in southern India, he is rapidly abandoning his vulture-habit and is reverting to stork-habit, finding his own food round ponds and marshes. In Africa they will remain near slaughter-houses for weeks on end, strutting about in complete indifference to man. At Nanyuki in Kenya I have seen over fifty of these horrible birds sitting about round offal, gorged and scarcely deigning to get out of the way of passers-by.

In many parts of the world the raven (*C. corax*) is a regular attendant at slaughter-houses; but *Corvus rhipidurus* is not interested in them.

Opening of milk bottles

During the past thirty years, the opening of milk bottles by birds is a most interesting aspect of birds making use of man. A restricted use of card-disc sealing of milk bottles commenced just before 1905; the practice was developed up to 1914 and was in regular use by 1918. By 1925 all the larger dairymen went over to card-disc sealing.

Hinde and Fisher (*British Birds*, 1949, p. 347, and again 1951, p. 393) and Rothschild and Clay in *F.F. and C.* have summarised this aspect of autolycism. The first record of birds opening milk bottles occurred at Swathling near Southampton in 1921 when birds were observed to drink milk. The practice is now common in many parts of Britain and has spread to Sweden, Denmark and Holland.

Ruwet (*Gerfaut*, 1953, p. 168) acquits Belgian tits of opening milk bottles, for these are not left out of doors in Belgium and are closed by mechanical or metallic caps, but a series of tests show that they learn to open bottles stopped with cardboard in a few days and show initiative, adaptation and visual imitation, the blue tit learning the most quickly.

On the Continent metal-foil stoppers are in general use. The habit spread to blue, great and coal tits and to a lesser extent to house sparrows, blackbirds, starlings, robins, chaffinches and hedge-sparrows. On the Continent jackdaws, magpies and greater spotted woodpeckers have adopted the habit, whilst in America there is a single case of Steller's jay (*Cyanocitta*) at Seattle.

In some cases tits have followed a milkman's cart down the street and have removed tops of bottles in the cart whilst the man delivers milk to the houses.

PLATE 43

Bird at milk bottle

Hinde and Fisher, in trying to account for this peculiar habit, make a hypothetical suggestion.

1. The initial investigation of the milk bottle by the pioneers can probably be understood on the basis of the normal innate feeding behaviour.
2. The subsequent return of these individuals to milk is probably due to trial-and-error learning.
3. The apparent copying of the behaviour by other individuals is probably due to another process—local enhancement—which modifies the appetitive behaviour of feeding and is initially independent of reward.

I believe the explanation to be simpler and to be derived from a desire for liquid. Birds, especially in built-up areas where these sealed bottles are in use, are often short of water; the milk can be seen through the glass and is recognised as liquid; birds, at least those in my London garden, will take milk in preference to water if the two are laid out side by side; it is a bird's natural instinct to hammer away at something which obstructs drinking. In hot weather tits will hammer fruit to get at moisture (fruit-juice). If water is provided, the destruction of fruit ceases. That is my experience.

In my London garden I placed a dairy foil-stoppered glass bottle on my bird table. The stopper was pierced by jays, blue tits and a robin, and in each case they were seen to drink milk. On the following day I placed a brown earthenware jar full of milk and stoppered with foil on my bird table. The birds could not see the milk and it was untouched though available for three days. A jay even sat on the bottle without disturbing the foil cover.

Tits have long since abandoned the principle that private property is private; their delinquencies have gone from bad to worse; we should not blame a thirsty bird for raiding our milk, even though water is readily obtainable, but they are now entering post boxes and tearing letters to pieces. Logan Home (Bambrough Conference 1952) attributed the reprehensible habit of tearing paper to boredom; tits, like naughty children devoid of occupation and with nothing to do, turn to destruction. But tits have gone further than acts prompted by boredom—they have attacked corks in sherry bottles, surely prompted by something more exciting than boredom; an inebriated tit would indeed be a delight. Other tits have torn the backs of books, stripped off wallpaper, scattered the pins from a cushion and raided a kitchen. If these practices continue and develop, no room with open windows will be safe unless netted and I fear that in many cases counter-action will be taken by persons who prefer good bindings to tits; we cannot spank tits or send them to gaol.

Attracted by disturbance

The Siberian jay (*Cractes*) in both Europe and America will follow man in forest, hoping to profit by disturbance; in Finland, on more than one occasion, small parties of this bird would be attracted by a shot and sometimes they would follow one about for miles.

Jackson (*Ibis*, 1945, pp. 284-6) records the carmine bee-eater following both man and motor vehicles for disturbed insects.

Recently in Manipur, when I was plodding through swamps of water hyacinth (*Eichornia*), both swallows and sand martins congregated round my legs catching disturbed insects, in one case passing through my legs as I stood purposely with legs apart.

On the Athi Plains when shooting quail (*Coturnix delagorguei*) a pair of lanner falcon circled above the line of guns and stooped time and again at quail flushed by the advancing party, eventually securing a bird each, but in most cases the quail were too quick and would dive into the grass. The disadvantage to the guns was that quail which appreciated the situation would not rise.

Under this heading may be cited a curious case of falcons taking advantage of trains on the Uganda Railway, especially between Voi and Tsavo. On several occasions I have seen a pair of lanner (*F. biarmicus*) waiting on the train and stooping at doves, rollers and other birds which sit on telegraph posts and fly off as the train disturbs them. They would also attend a safari, in the old days when travelling in Kenya was undertaken on foot, in the hopes of securing prey disturbed by the long line of porters. I have also seen bateleur (*Terathopius*) attend safaris for the same purpose.

During a hare drive in Ross-shire on the freshly snow-covered mountains in November, a pair of golden eagles (*Aquila chrysaëtos*) appeared. Many hares were on the move, lolloping about like white rabbits, but the eagles would not exert themselves over these. They would wait until a wounded hare fell or struggled just out of gun-shot range and would then come down with a swoop and carry off the prize. I never grudged those eagles their bad manners, but some of my guests would be most indignant and could not understand the pleasure it gave me to see my game carried off by 'vermin.'

In British Somaliland, not far from Hargeisa, is a famous watering-place for sandgrouse. So soon as shooting commences any tawny or steppe eagles in the neighbourhood fly to the sound of the guns and take up positions on thorn trees and go off at once after a wounded bird. The guns employ small boys to retrieve birds. On one occasion I witnessed a race between a small boy and a steppe eagle after a wounded bird, the boy using a switch to keep the eagle off and the eagle buffeting the boy with its wings in its efforts to get the bird.

In India I have seen a tawny eagle (*Aquila rapax*) swoop down on an Alpine swift and carry it off after it had fallen to my gun, an annoying experience, for I wanted the specimen badly and such a small bird was a poor meal for an eagle.

Rand (*Fieldiana*, 1954, p. 18) records the goshawk, usually a shy bird of the forests, becoming interested in man and following him about. In Alberta a juvenile came flying to perch in a tree overhead and peered down at the intruder. Rand had seen young goshawks approach a man, scream at him and even follow him through the forest, flying from tree to tree.

In North Uist and in Orkney I have been accompanied, when snipe shooting, by hen-harrier who would invariably follow a pricked bird and on one occasion retrieved a dead bird within easy shot of me.

I have also been pestered by pallid harriers (*Circus macrourus*) in Egypt when quail shooting. It is true they made the birds lie, but to have dead birds taken from under my nose was sometimes more than my patience could stand.

When a party of eight guns commenced to shoot at dawn on the Horse-shoe Jhil near Delhi in 1913 there was not a harrier in the air, but by 9 a.m. there was a huge concentration of both pallid and other harriers, all busy picking up pricked birds, doubtless attracted by the sound of the guns.

Pallid harriers in the Sudan have been seen patrolling telegraph wires regularly, searching for birds injured by flying into them.

Under this heading may have come a habit developed by the bateleur eagle (*Terathopius*) in Kenya between Nyeri and Nanyuki. There is considerable night traffic by car and many hares and other rodents are killed, with an occasional owl, nightjar, or snake. The bateleur has learned to patrol this road, roosting on a telegraph pole near the road so as to be on the scene at the crack of dawn; so soon as it is light they pass up and down the road in pairs, circling and soaring. In 1949 three pairs were patrolling the road and I was assured by local residents that it is done regularly throughout the year.

On 8 March 1945 I was returning from the Isles of Scilly and passed through the scene of two destroyers resting on their laurels after having "killed" a submarine. The sea was strewn with oil and wreckage, among which were thousands of dead pilchard killed by depth charges; they were distributed over about two square miles; birds of all description were feeding on them, the vast majority being kittiwake (*Rissa*) and herring gull (*argentatus*), a few greater black-backed gulls (*marinus*); no common gulls (*canus*), cormorants (*P. carbo*) or shags (*P. aristotelis*). There were two great skua (*Stercorarius*) and a few smaller skua which I failed to identify. Many razorbill (*Alca torda*) were gorging on fish, with some lying exhausted or dead from excess. There were hundreds of gannets (*Sula*) and I counted twenty-seven great northern diver (*Colymbus*). Both these normally obtain their food by diving but here they were gobbling dead fish from the surface. Long before we reached the site of the battle I had noticed a general trend of flight of many species, attracted not by the sight of fish but by other birds also converging on the scene—birds attracting birds—as is the vulture's habit. And long after leaving the site, even as far distant as Mount's Bay, birds were still converging towards the feast.

The initial attraction in the Scilly example may have been exploding depth charges.

This is confirmed by Vleugel (*Brit. B.*, 1951, p. 180), who noted 'large numbers of gulls, most of them apparently herring gulls (*L. argentatus*) coming from all directions to the scene of an explosion to feed on dead fish in Holland. After some time they disappeared to return again when another explosion took place.' A similar case is mentioned by Berlepsch (*Journ. f. Orn.*, LVIII, p. 98). The ivory gull (*Pagophila*) in northern Norway is in the habit of coming to look for blood and remains of seals when a shot has been fired.

In the Orkneys, when I was fishing for sea trout, a seal with full knowledge of angling would watch me from about 200 yards, and so soon as a fish was hooked he would submerge, snatch my hooked fish, break me and then appear again from his stance to watch for a second chance. Irrelevant but apt.

Following the plough

I do not know when following the plough became an almost universal habit among birds to whom up-turned soil is an attraction. Rooks (*C. frugilegus*) and jackdaws (*C. monedula*) have certainly practised it in Britain for centuries but I do not recollect seeing gulls follow the plough until the first few years of this century; in fact, the gull was not an inland bird in winter during my boyhood when we lived on the Test in Hampshire. Never once did we see a gull of any sort at any time of year and now they abound from autumn to early spring.

I have seen black-headed (*ribibundus*), herring- and lesser black-backed (*argentatus-fuscus* group) and common (*canus*) following ploughs, but never the greater black-backed (*marinus* and *hyperboreus*). Kittiwakes (*Rissa*) never. In Sweden the little gull (*minutus*) occasionally does so. So eager and greedy do gulls become when leather-jackets are turned up, that cases have occurred of them becoming caught up in the machinery of the plough or buried by upturned sods. In Devon I have seen a buzzard come down to a gull which had been disabled by such an accident. Several cases of buzzard following the plough for grubs and worms have been recorded.

I have seen kestrels (*Falco tinnunculus*) hovering and feeding behind a plough in Ireland. Starlings (*Sturnus*), fieldfares and missel-thrushes (*Turdus pilaris* and *viscivorus*) frequently do so, and of course the magpie (*Pica*). In the Pyrenees and Himalayas the chough (*Pyrrhocorax*) does so, and in the Aden Protectorate I have seen the fan-tailed raven (*rhipidurus*) do so. In India gulls have not yet learned the habit.

The mynah (*Acridotheres*) follows the plough in Kashmir and I have seen rooks and jackdaws doing so in Afghanistan.

Wilkinson (*Brit. Birds*, 1951, p. 204) records swallows, house martins and sand martins following a tractor and catching moths (*Plusia gamma*).

Grass fires

Grass fires started by man will attract all kinds of birds—kites (*Milvus*), kestrels (*Falco tinnunculus*), hobbies (*Falco subbuteo*), pratincoles (*Glareola*) and owls (*Asio accipitrinus* and *helvola*), which march to the smoke and prey on flying insects disturbed by the fire. In Kenya I have often attracted swifts (*Apus*) by starting a fire; they come as readily to a fire as they do to a sudden rain-storm, and for the same reason. On more than one occasion both the great bustard (*A. kori*) and secretary birds (*Sagittarius*) would fly towards it to feast on locusts, lizards and snakes disturbed by the heat. In India a jungle or scrub fire will attract rollers, drongos and shrikes.

The last phase

The final end of man; corpses burned on pyres beside the holy Ganges and thrown into the river are often stranded on sand-banks; these macerated and liquefying human bodies are then slopgobbled by ruddy sheld-duck (*Casarca*).

In Bombay until recently there were Towers of Silence on top of which the Parsee community placed their dead; vultures would congregate and tear these corpses to pieces, sometimes carrying off tit-bits which were dropped in private gardens. It was no uncommon shock to find the unashamed odds and ends of Mr Readymoney Bhoy outside one's dining-room.

The case of Indicator, the honey-guide

The case of the honey-guides (*Indicator*) is exceptional. They have an association with honey-bees, with man and probably with small mammals; and they also parasitise other birds when breeding. There is quite a literature on the subject to which I shall contribute my own experience on the subject.

When living in the Nandi country in December 1905 I wrote in my diary:

I had the most delightful experience today with a honey-guide (*Indicator indicator*). Whilst working in the forest I became aware that a small bird was endeavouring to attract my attention by chattering at me from only a few feet distance, evidently in a great state of excitement; it would fly away into the forest but always in the same direction. He was so persistent that I decided to follow him; his excitement then increased and he would keep some twenty yards ahead of me usually rather high up in a tree but he never for a moment lost sight of me; after some 150 yards he was joined by two others and their united chorus left me in no doubt as to the direction they wished me to take; the three birds finally came to rest in a smallish tree and as they refused to leave it I was convinced that the honey they required was near at hand; a short inspection found the bees' nest under a strip of rotten bark and my men soon laid it bare and spread the comb, rich with golden honey, on the ground.

As soon as it was clear to the birds that we had located the honey, they sat fairly

194

still in the tree within a few feet of us with obvious feelings of satisfaction; their little breasts were puffed out and they would often throw their heads back and utter a low churning sound; but their greed was not untempered with jealousy, for, with an angry call, one would lift the feathers of his crown and make a dash at one of the others; then would ensue a regular scurry through the surrounding trees, but all three would soon return to watch anxiously our operations; having spread out the comb on a bare piece of ground we sat and watched from a distance of some twenty-five yards. The birds came down at once but would not feed on the ground, each taking a large piece of comb and flying off with it out of sight; and so soon as they had finished that bit they returned for more; I tried to follow one to see it feed, but could not locate it in the thick foliage.

There is no doubt that these birds deliberately attracted my attention in order that I should follow their guidance to the bees which they had already located. The bird knows his job and is almost human in its guidance.

My men tell me that if, after finding honey and none is left for the birds, their next act of guidance will be to a snake or some noxious beast. But I fancy this is pure imagination, for none could quote an instance.

On two other occasions in Kenya I have followed this bird in forest, once for about fifty yards and on the other occasion for over 200 yards but either my own ineptitude or bad guidance failed to find the bees' nest.

I am also well acquainted with *Indicator variegatus* and *I. minor* in the field, but have never noticed any attempt on their part to attract my attention.

In Kenya it is the custom of the natives to place hollow logs in trees to attract bees. I have often been present when natives have opened up the bees' nests in the logs to secure honey and though *Indicator* is fairly common I have never seen them take the slightest interest in the proceeding.

The experiences of others closely agree with the one I have related above.

The habit probably originated from the assistance given to the bird by mammals, before man came on the scene. The honey badger has given us a clue. Stephenson Hamilton in *Animal Life in Africa*, p. 248, relates:

You may be resting in the bush in the cool of the afternoon, or on some cloudy day, when your attention is arrested by the persistent and approaching chatter of one of these feathered spies. Presently the bird itself comes fluttering on to a branch some thirty yards distant, where it perches, flapping its wings, and displaying every sign of impatience. For a moment it is silent, and then a less familiar sound strikes the ear; a light sibilant hissing and chuckling, which at first you find yourself unable to identify: Kru-tshee, kru-tshee-clk, clk, clk, whee-tshee-tse, tse-whi-o-o (it is almost impossible to do it justice on paper). The honey-guide understands, and having, with undulating flight, sought another tree some thirty yards further on, renews his invitation. Keeping quite still, and looking steadily, you presently spy a little grey and black form, moving along at a steady jog-trot; the tail is carried slightly above the level of the back, and the head, except when raised to glance up at the guide, is held a little low. Every time the bird utters his monotonous refrain, which, translated into feathered language, means 'Come along, come along, don't be so slow,' the follower replies 'All right, my friend, don't be alarmed, I am coming.' And thus the strange procession passes out of sight to the hollow log, where the unlucky insects are industriously slaving, only ultimately to satisfy the appetites of bird and beast. When following the honey-guide, the natives of many tribes in Africa endeavour to imitate the curious whistling and chuckling sounds of the ratel; though indeed the bird appears to require but little encouragement to keep it to its work.

Friedmann (*U.S. Nat. Mus. Bull.*, 1955, Bull. No. 208) gives a valuable summary of all that is known about *Indicator*, both their brood parasitism and their guiding habit. He does not agree that there is any purpose or plan in the guiding, whilst the role of the ratel as a follower in the guiding process seems now conclusively established. Bees-wax and not the honey appears to be the choice. A captive *Indicator* lived for thirty-two days on nothing but wax.

Birds making use of man for protection

On the Tibetan plateau, where no cover exists, a hoopoe was caught in the open by a falcon. It at once flew to a mounted officer and sought refuge in his saddle, where it remained until the hawk made off. A rather similar case occurred in Syria near Damascus when two starlings took refuge from a hawk and entered my motor car, both allowing themselves to be caught sooner than risk the greater danger of being eaten.

Man making use of birds

The baby being carried by a white stork is an old Nordic myth, connected with the most important event in man's life. Man also makes use of birds in many ways, foremost for food; the domestication of the rock pigeon, grey-lag goose, the mallard, the Muscovy duck, the turkey, jungle fowl and guineafowl has largely added to man's varied diet. For sport we breed large numbers of birds for the pleasure of killing them, we breed ostriches for their feathers and hides, we kill others for their decorative plumes and we train hawks to kill other birds. We also keep large numbers of birds in confinement, canaries, parrots and the host of wild birds in various Zoological Gardens, a degrading sight and of little scientific value. And finally we have trained the rock pigeon to carry messages long distances.

An amusing incident occurred at the Paris Peace Conference during 1919 with reference to carrier pigeons. A file was started in all seriousness, suggesting that if a talking parrot could be crossed with a carrier pigeon, the hybrid might not only carry but deliver a verbal message. The first few criticisms were written in all seriousness and it was suggested that the London Zoo might carry out experiments. Arthur Hardinge thought it most 'reprehensible.' As it was known that I was interested in birds it was referred to me. In all seriousness I pointed out the absurdity of the suggestion.

I quote from that fascinating book *The Sea Around Us* by Rachael Carson (1952, p. 211):

> Students of primitive navigation believe that the migrations of birds had meaning for the Polynesians, and that they learned much from watching the flocks that gathered each year in the spring and fall, launched out over the ocean, and returned later out of the emptiness into which they had vanished. Harold Gatty believes the Hawaiians may have found their islands by following the spring migration of the golden plover from Tahiti to the Hawaiian chain, as the birds returned to the North American mainland. He has also suggested that the migratory path of the shining cuckoo may have guided other colonists from the Solomons to New Zealand.

Noah on his ark made use of birds and there is evidence to show that the Vikings used birds to locate land.

In the *Norway Pilot* we read of Jan Mayen Island that the presence of sea-fowl in large numbers will give an indication of the approach to land, and the noise of their rookeries may be useful in locating the shore.

And of Bear Island, that the sea around the islands teems with guillemots. These flocks and the direction of their flight on approaching, together with the use of the lead, are of great value in making the island when it is foggy.

And the *United States Pilot for Antarctica* says: 'Navigators should observe the bird life . . . shags are a sure sign of the proximity to land . . . the snowy petrel is invariably associated with ice and is of great interest to mariners as an augury of ice conditions in their course.'

BIRDS MAKING USE OF MAMMALS

For warmth

THE case of *Buphagus* roosting on a camel's back is mentioned under *Buphagus*.

Ernest Thompson Seton records a cowbird (*Molothrus ater*) surviving the winter at Winnipeg by warming itself on a bison's back and sleeping in a hollow it had made in the beast's hair.

For nesting

Both *Corvus albus* and *capensis* have been recorded by van Someren as removing hair from living sheep and goats for nesting material. Harris (*Auk*, 1946, p. 590) records the crow (*C. brachyrhynchus*) plucking hairs from cattle— 'Each crow had a beak full of white hairs from the cow's back,' and the cow paid no attention. Several cases have been recorded of jackdaws pulling hair from sheep and cattle for nesting purposes.

Van Someren has recorded the tit (*P. albiventris*) taking hair from a bushbuck, and another tit (*P. fringillinus*) taking wool from a sheep. In Britain I have seen the crested tit (*Parus cristatus*) removing hairs from the skin of a red deer in May, and in Hampshire I have seen the blue tit (*P. caeruleus*) removing hairs for its nest from a dead squirrel, returning time after time and working with furious energy. The kite (*Milvus migrans*) has been seen taking hair from a sick cow in Kenya, and in Arabia the same kite was seen tearing wool from a dead camel and flying off with it to its nest under construction. Riney (*Condor*, 1951, pp. 178–85), in a paper dealing with a bird–deer relationship, and with particular reference to mule deer, quotes eleven species of American birds in whose nests the hair of deer has been found.

Many birds breed down rodent burrows: several species of chats (*Oenanthe*), the small ground chough (*Podoces humilis*) of Tibet, shearwaters (*Puffinus*), the burrowing owl (*Athene cunicularia*) and many others. Axtell (*Auk*, 1955, p. 84) records the bronzed grackle nesting in an unoccupied beaver lodge in Ontario. As many as three beavers were seen at one time swimming within a few yards of the grackle on her nest. Sheld-duck have been found nesting down foxes' earths, and in Ladak I found the ruddy sheld–duck (*Casarca*) nesting down marmot burrows.

For protection against sun and wind

In Somaliland I have seen the small raven (*C. edithae*) with open beaks taking advantage during noonday sun of the shade given by camels; in Arabia I have seen a flock of short-toed larks (*Calandrella*) sheltering from the sun in the shade cast by sheep, and moving along with them as they fed, and on one occasion a small flock of migrating dunlin (*Erolia alpina*) came to rest in the shade of a motor car, completely exhausted and unafraid, drinking greedily from a small pan of water put out for their benefit. I have also seen this same bird at Rutbah in the Syrian Desert come to water in the courtyard of a large building.

In South Uist during a gale, when the shore was drenched with spray and spume, I have seen turnstones (*Arenaria interpres*) and purple sandpiper (*Erolia maritima*) sheltering behind Highland cattle lying down on grassland.

For convenience

Many birds attendant on animals for food will rest and preen on the beasts they attend, but a case of pure convenience, without desire for food, is Huxley's record (*Ibis*, 1945, p. 471, with illustration) of a vulture perched on the back of a sheep in the Gold Coast. It is interesting as showing an apparent in-difference on the part of the sheep to such a large rider; and was prompted probably for no other reason than convenience, for every large raptor prefers sitting on some eminence rather than on the ground on account of the length of its tail.

About fifteen miles from the mainland and at the mouth of the Rufiji River in Tanganyika Territory lies a small flat island called Mafia. I visited it in 1915 and was surprised to see a school of hippopotami on the coral reef about 500 yards off shore, and in salt water. How they got there I cannot imagine, but the Africans told me they had been there as far back as their memories could take them and that they always spent the day in the salt water, coming ashore at night and doing much damage to crops. On the same coral reef were several crab plover (*Dromas*), and at high tide they would fly on to

O

the backs of the hippopotami, using them purely as resting-places. There was no resentment on the part of the pachyderm.

Capt. Pitman (in litt.) informs me that he has seen wagtails (*vidua* and *flava*), the pied kingfisher (*Ceryle rudis*), the Egyptian goose (*Alopochen*), tree-duck (*Dendrocygna fulva*), the small cormorant (*P. africanus*), the darter (*Anhinga*) and the common sandpiper (*Tringa hypoleuca*) on hippopotami basking on the surface.

For food

In British Somaliland I have seen several of the small raven (*Corvus edithae*) riding on camels, piercing grain sacks and greedily devouring the contents. North (*Ibis*, 1944, p. 175) records the same raven pecking a sheep's back in Somaliland and drawing blood, and on another occasion a raven 'landed on the back of a moving camel, which was being led by its owner, and started pecking its back.' It refused to stop until the owner turned and chased it away; in neither case was it clear whether the host's parasites or the host's own flesh were being eaten.

I have seen a hooded crow (*C. cornix*) on a donkey in Ireland; it seemed to be searching for something in the hair of the back, but was not seen to eat anything. In Manipur I have seen the jungle crow (*C. macrorhynchus*) picking ticks off water buffalo, as many as four birds on one beast. On one occasion they evicted a cattle egret (*Ardeola ibis*) which was resting on the rump of the beast. Jackdaws (*C. monedula*) commonly attend cattle and donkeys, and have been recorded on deer in Savernake Forest, the animals much appreciating the attention.

I have seen jackdaws delousing sheep on many occasions, sometimes as many as five or six birds on each animal, exploring every part of the animal for ticks and parasites, the sheep paying not the slightest attention. Only once, in Ireland, did I see resentment by an old ram, but he had excuse, for he was making love and disliked any form of distraction.

Bent (*Bull. U.S. Nat. Mus.*, 1946, pp. 191, 149) records the American magpie (*Pica p. hudsonia*) examining domestic stock for parasites and probing sores to eat the animal's flesh and blood, sometimes causing death among sheep. They have also been seen on wapiti and wild sheep, when their presence is resented by the animal. During the time when buffalo were abundant, large flocks would follow hunting parties for refuse and would alight on horses with sore backs and peck the sores until the death of the animal ensued. This magpie used to be more numerous than at present, perching freely on deer, wild sheep and bison, pecking insects off the back. But now they have taken to sheep, causing death by attacking the kidneys. European magpies will attend and perch on the backs of most domestic animals; I have seen them on reindeer, on yaks, on domestic cattle, donkeys and camels. Delmee (*Gerfaut*, xxxv, p. 187) records a magpie extracting larval parasites from the hides of cattle. They have also been seen pecking for parasites on deer in Savernake Forest.

In *British Birds*, 1944, p. 99, is a note on parasites taken by magpies and jackdaws from sheep and other animals. The insects chiefly taken are the sheep ked (*Melophagus ovinus*). The less common biting louse (*Trichodectes sphoerocephalus*) is rarely met with in these birds' stomachs. Attempts by both jackdaws and magpies to perch on horses is resented.

Jays (*Aphelocoma*) have been seen in America searching for ectoparasites on the backs of deer.

Charles Lane (*Ibis*, 1957, p. 116) describes how he saw a pair of Alpine chough (*Pyrrhocorax graculus*) following a stoat in alpine Switzerland, and when it entered a hole after rodents, the chough would wait outside and then follow it to the next hole. He also records the Alpine chough as preying on nestlings of the snow finch (*Montifringilla*).

The starling (*Sturnus vulgaris*) throughout its range attends cattle and sheep, sometimes pecking at ectoparasites, sometimes resting and preening and sometimes attending them on the ground, searching for disturbed insect life. In Arabia I have seen them attending both camels and donkeys. In Sweden I have seen them on pigs, busily pecking at and eating sucking lice (*Haematopinus*), some of which were recovered in a damaged state from the gullet of a shot bird. In South Uist I found no fewer than seventeen large ticks in the stomach of a single starling shot immediately after a long attendance on sheep.

The marsh mynah (*Sturnus contra*) has been seen picking ticks off water buffalo in Manipur. And a mynah (*Aethiopsar fuscus*) is a constant attendant on the Indian rhinoceros and wild water-buffalo in Assam.

The case of the ox-pecker (*Buphagus*) is dealt with separately.

Cowbirds (*Molothrus*) gather about grazing cattle, feeding on disturbed insects and often perching on the backs of cattle and feeding on flies, etc. The starling (*Sturnus vulgaris*) is developing a similar habit in America.

Pipits and wagtails constantly attend domestic stock and wild animals, catching disturbed insects. In Manipur the pipit (*A. roseatus*) was in constant attendance on water-buffalo. The yellow wagtails, *M. flava* and *citreola* in particular, and *M. clara* in South Africa, will sometimes form dense flocks round grazing animals. In Arabia I have experienced the greatest difficulty in securing specimens of migrant *M. flava* owing to their refusal to leave the close proximity of sheep. The pied wagtails (*M. alba* and *maderaspatensis*) seldom attend grazing stock and I have only once seen the grey wagtail (*M. cinerea*) attending an animal, a pig in a farmyard in West Ireland, when the wagtail was actually picking flies off the legs and jumping up to the rump to secure insects. The pig was quite indifferent.

The bulbul (*Irena cyanogaster*) is recorded by Stott (*Auk*, 1947, p. 130) as attending the monkey *Macacarinus*, waiting on them for disturbed insects and falling fruit and possibly acting as sentinels.

Drongos are commonly seen in India on the backs of domestic stock and on rhinoceros and wild water-buffalo, sallying forth from their stance to pick up insects disturbed by grazing. Heinrich in Stresemann (*Journ. f. Orn.*, 1940, p. 34) records the drongo (*D. hottentottus*) accompanying monkeys (*Cynopithecus*) in Celebes, and another drongo (*Dissemurus paradiseus*) following macaque monkeys in Borneo.

It is on record that the robin (*Erithacus*) will watch the burrowing activities of the mole (*Talpa*), profiting by pouncing on worms driven to the surface and even seizing a worm from the mouth of a surfaced mole. I have not seen this myself.

Most of the swallow family (*Hirundinidae*) will attend grazing animals for disturbed insects. In Swedish Lapland and on the Lake of Antioch I have seen sand-martins (*Riparia*) so thick round grazing cattle that at a distance it seemed as though there was a dark halo round the beasts.

The kea parrot (*Nestor*) of New Zealand certainly has an association with sheep which has developed into a liking for mutton and persecution of the kea. I have heard two explanations of this habit, which can only have developed during the last hundred years.

The first is that the kea found a food he relished in scraps of fat remaining on the skins of sheep hung up to dry and, associating this food with the living sheep, perched on its back and dug in to get the food. The second explanation is that the habit has developed more out of devilry than malice. It is asserted that the kea at one time found delight in perching on the backs of sheep just to take a joy-ride. The sheep would stampede and the kea with his powerful pointed bill would have to hang on, often penetrating the skin of the back and giving him a taste for mutton which he followed up by deliberately perching on sheep to take a meal off the living animal. It is not a universal habit among the kea population and is confined to certain individuals who have become sheep-eaters. But it has led to wholesale persecution. I am glad to say the kea is holding his own.

The carmine bee-eater (*Merops nubicus*), in addition to riding on birds, has also been seen riding on donkeys, sheep and camels for disturbed insects, but never more than one bird on one animal and the bird always returning to its own mount.

The case of the white-crested hornbill (*Berenicornis albocristatus*) of West Africa is well known, the birds associating with monkeys but remaining at a lower level and availing themselves of dropped fruit and disturbed insects. Chapin (*B. Congo*, II, p. 352) says: 'habit of following monkeys and eating disturbed insects.' Petit (*Mem. Soc. Zool. France*, XII, p. 68) says of this hornbill: 'usually with monkeys but at lower levels; I have often seen them catch fruit dropped by the monkeys.' Petit also records another hornbill (*Ceratogymna atrata*) on large trees with monkeys with which it plays.

On two occasions I have seen colobus monkeys on Mount Kenya attended by the hornbill (*Bycanistes brevis*). On both occasions the birds kept at a lower level than the monkeys and were constantly dropping to the ground to pick up fruit discarded by the monkeys. Sometimes a hornbill would ascend to monkey-level. Colobus has a long flowing tail and the hornbill has an extremely powerful bill combined with a sense of humour. Whether from devilry or in retaliation for grimaces or to spur the monkeys to greater efforts, a hornbill with his huge hops would get among the monkeys, trying to tweak their tails and generally producing pandemonium, and having achieved his object would gracefully float down to his own level or to the ground.

Rand (*Auk*, 1953, pp. 26-30) deals with the factors affecting the feeding rate of the ani (*Crotophaga sulcirostris*). They often accompany cattle and mules for the insects these animals disturb; though they often settle on animals' backs it is doubtful if they search for parasites. They also follow

203

ants for the insects and other small animals driven from hiding by the ants; the association with cattle is entirely to the ani's advantage.

Elton instances kites (*Milvus*) following elephants in the Sudan and feeding on disturbed insects (*Anim. Ecology*, 3rd impr. 1947, p. 67), and I have seen lesser kestrel (*Falco naumanni*) in Nyasaland waiting on a herd of buffalo and catching locusts disturbed as beasts grazed.

Elton (*op. cit.*) also records herons (*Ardea*) following elephants for disturbed insects. The African heron (*A. melanocephala*) has been seen attending both eland and buffalo for disturbed insects.

The most persistent animal-attendant is the cattle egret (*Ardeola ibis*). In Manipur and in Egypt they live out their lives with domestic stock, roosting in neighbouring trees, breeding near by, flying out to cattle as they leave the byres and retiring to roost when the cattle are driven home in the evening. They readily sit on grazing animals; I have seen them on camels near Port Sudan, on the wild camels of southern Spain, on elephants and on the Indian rhinoceros. Capt. Pitman has seen them on the white rhinoceros and elephants in the Sudan. Their normal technique is walking close to grazing animals and feeding on disturbed insects; though there are many records of ticks being found in the stomachs of cattle egrets, there is no evidence of these being taken direct from the animal.

North (*Ibis*, 1945, p. 469) shows that out of 649 stomachs in Egypt not a single tick was present, and follows Chapin in finding them distasteful to the bird. Holman (*Ibis*, 1946, p. 232) does not think the cattle egret is immediately concerned with ticks but will take them when sufficiently attracted. He says: 'Ticks on the underparts of the animals are very numerous and it is interesting to see a bird inspecting a crowd of ticks and apparently selecting the more attractive,' and again, 'I never saw a bird searching an animal's back for parasites; my impression is that ticks on animals' backs are few.' Wild birds, breeding in the Giza Zoological Gardens near Cairo, have been seen on the back of a captive hippopotamus; and in the Basle Zoo some cattle egrets took a fancy to a capybara, walked up to this uncouth rat and sat on it, the rat not minding in the least.

Snowy egrets (*Egretta thula*) attend cattle in America, feeding on grass-hoppers and flies but not eating ticks. And both this heron and the little blue heron (*Florida thula*) occasionally follow pigs in Florida (Rand ex. Howell, *Fieldiana*, 1954, p. 21).

The little egret (*Egretta garzetta*) often attends both domestic and wild cattle and most large mammals but I have never seen them perch on animals; ticks have never been found in their stomachs, their activities being confined to insects disturbed by the mammal.

The sun-bittern (*Eurypyga helias*) is recorded by Verrill (*Strange Birds and their Stories*, 1938, pp. 153-60) as attending tapirs in South America: 'You may always be sure of finding sun-bitterns near tapirs . . . they go carefully over the beasts picking off parasites, the tapirs lying on their sides . . . the bird will utter its shrill cry of alarm and warn his big partner who at once seeks safety in the nearest stream.' Verrill assures his readers that if attended by a bittern, the tapir takes no precautions against danger.

On both the Victoria Nyanza and at the Murchison Falls I have seen both the common sandpiper and the ringed plover (*Ch. tricollaris*) on the backs of hippopotamus basking on the surface. On one occasion there were as many as seven common sandpiper on the beast, all busy picking away at congealed perspiration and eating it; I forced the pachyderm to submerge when all the birds flew to the near-by shore; but so soon as the beast surfaced again, the birds at once flew back and resumed their feast.

Phalaropes have been seen resting and preening on surfaced whales. The association between whales and phalaropes is a natural one, for both feed on plankton, and where this food is abundant these marine leviathans and this small elegant wader will be found gathered together in partnership.

In *Life* (14 Dec. 1953) is a photograph of a lily-trotter (*Actophilus africanus*) sitting on the head of a hippopotamus and picking at something in its ear. The black rail (*Limnocorax*) has also been observed on hippopotami.

Desmond Evans (*Field*, 24 Oct. 1957) records seals in Wales tossing fish into the air, a habit I have never observed, and gulls snatching the fish from the seal's jaws before he could swallow it. Gulls in the Arctic will attend the polar bear and gobble up the remains of his meal.

Simmons (*Brit. B.*, 1952, p. 469) records gannets, gulls and black terns following porpoises for food; in the Straits of Gibraltar I have seen gannets and gulls feeding greedily on the debris of fish after porpoises had feasted.

The association of birds with living whales is summarised by Routh (*Ibis*, 1949, p. 602), who says:

As many sorts of birds and whales feed on the same kind of food, it is not uncommon to see whales and birds together. Huge flocks of short-tailed shearwaters may be seen in the south during the southern summer congregated over a small patch of sea, constantly rising from and entering the water, while at the same time the backs and blasts of a school of Humpback Whales break surface among them. In these conditions it is clear that both birds and whales are feeding on a single patch of krill. It is hard to say whether both birds and whales arrived at the krill patch independently, or whether the birds use the whales as indicators of krill patches.

It is, however, certain that birds will sometimes follow whales, even when the latter are not feeding. Sooty albatrosses have been seen doing this over open sea, and a flock consisting of terns (possibly Arctic terns) and Antarctic petrels has been seen following a school of minke whales through pack ice. Both birds and whales were travelling, and it seems certain that the birds were following the whales deliberately. It is however doubtful whether birds follow whales simply in order to be led from one patch of krill to another, for these are extremely easy to sight from the air, and one would naturally believe birds could find them even more easily than whales. Prions and blue petrels have been observed flying round the small reddish-brown patches of whale excreta floating in the sea, and this no doubt indicates one cause of the association of some species of birds with whales. It seems, moreover, quite likely that this habit of some birds of following living whales may be exactly analogous with the case quoted by Elton, *Animal Ecology*, 3rd impression 1947, p. 67, of land birds (kites and grey herons) following elephants in the Sudan so as to feed off the insects disturbed by the animals' feet, and that the sea birds thus use the whales as another agent (like ships and icebergs) for raising inaccessible plankton to within their reach.

Acting as sentinels

Birds will alert many kinds of big game to the presence of man and other enemies, especially the larger cats. The cases I have come across are a sable in Rhodesia being alerted by a nightjar (*Cosmetornis*) which I disturbed. These birds do not fly by day unless disturbed, so a daylight flight would naturally be unusual and mean disturbance of some sort. Grouse alerting deer in Scotland is well known and deer move quickly before man comes into view. I have seen ibex alerted by snow-cock in Ladak and blackbuck alerted by sandgrouse suddenly rising in the middle of the day, a movement which can only have meant disturbance by some enemy.

Alarm among small birds is often followed by an unusual silence, especially in thick bush or forest; this is at once noticed by forest animals accustomed to a constant friendly twitter. I was once watching a bushbuck in fairly thick bush on the slopes of Mount Kenya; he was walking towards me but on coming within fifty yards and within the silent area, he was at once on the alert, though I was not aware of any warning bird-note; what the bushbuck suspected was some enemy which had produced a silent area.

For the case of *Buphagus*, see under that bird.

The cattle egret serves as a sentinel to elephant, buffalo and blackbuck, all of which I have witnessed. If buffalo are attended by egrets they are restful—not constantly throwing up their heads—and when stalking them one must stalk the egrets, not the buffalo.

In southern Spain I had an interesting experience with the wild camels of the Marismas. We were anxious to get to close quarters for photography. A party of five camels which usually make off at half a mile when sighting a human being, were attended by a dozen or so egrets. We used stalking ponies, walking on their off side, and when we were within about 300 yards of the camels two egrets flew towards us, making for a herd of domestic cattle about half a mile away; on flying over us and discovering the ruse, they banked heavily and flew off at a tangent. The camels, quietly browsing, spotted this at once, threw up their heads and made off, splashing their lumbering way through swamp.

In Nyasaland, when trying to get at a large bull buffalo, I had to wait for over an hour before the attendant egrets moved; they were suspicious as they had seen me from about 400 yards, and whilst one sat as sentinel on the bull's back, the others fed around the beast. Eventually the bull lay down and the egrets moved to other buffalo. I then had no difficulty in approaching my large bull.

It is doubtful whether birds (except perhaps *Buphagus*) consciously alarm game out of sympathy or from a desire to protect animals from whom they derive benefit. It is more likely that wild animals are extremely alert to danger of any sort and that any movement of birds which denotes alarm is infectious.

THE CASE OF *BUPHAGUS*

There are two species of ox-peckers or tick-birds, the red-billed (*B. erythrorhynchus*) and the yellow-billed (*B. africanus*), the former occurring from the southern Sudan and Eritrea to Natal, and the latter occurring throughout the greater part of Africa south of the Sahara but not in thick forest. But they are now becoming scarce in South Africa owing to dipping of domestic stock and absence of wild game; they are abundant in the Kruger National Park where wild game still exists.

They belong to the starling family and have been variously named ox-peckers, tick-birds and rhinoceros birds. I have spent eleven years in various parts of Africa and have devoted much attention to these interesting birds, mostly in relation to big game.

Where the two species occur in more or less the same district, the red-billed is usually at higher altitudes. I have seen them at 11,000 feet on eland in the Aberdare Mountains.

Food

When I was stationed at Fort Hall and Nyeri in 1904 I made me a dummy ostrich, the skin of a hen bird stretched on a frame, the head and neck carried by hand. This disguise enabled me to approach game in open country so long as I moved up wind. I was thus able to watch both species of tick-bird at very close quarters.

Both species search for ticks, flies and lice; these are sometimes swallowed, presumably if gorged, but more often a tick is removed, flicked off by a shake of the head and the open wound then sucked; as a tick injects something to prevent coagulation of blood, a wound runs for some time after a tick-bite. They will attack, and keep open, sores on a rhinoceros, sometimes pecking hard and sometimes just sucking the oozing blood. It is not proved that they will actually start a sore and dig for blood. They will swallow sucking lice from warthog.

An investigation in Tanganyika about 1933 showed that of 58 examined, 55 contained over 2,000 ticks in their stomachs; of these ticks, 95 per cent were found to be a species which carries East Coast fever.

Van Someren (*E. Afr. Agr. J.*, 1951) has investigated the food of the red-billed and agrees that ticks form the main diet and that birds tend to become scarce on domestic stock where dipping is prevalent; and that they will reopen sores and feed on exuding blood. Perhaps new sores are made.

In the old days of pack mules and donkeys in East Africa, many animals died (*teste* Jackson 1938) entirely through the attention of *Buphagus*.

Both species, mostly red-billed, come readily to slaughter-houses (Nanyuki and British Somaliland), where they will feed on blood off freshly flayed hides.

I have never seen them actually take flesh nor has it been proved that they peck flesh from an open sore on a living beast.

On two occasions north of Nyeri in Kenya I have seen yellow-billed drinking at a stream at noon in a compact flock. I have never seen red-billed drink but have seen them bathing and splashing in a rain puddle.

Nests and their reaction

The yellow-billed are usually on larger game and domestic stock; I have never seen them on anything smaller than a donkey. Red-billed will feed on almost any animal, from hippopotamus, black and white rhinoceros and buffalo, to roan and sable, not bothering much about the smaller antelope. Zebra are only used if other game is not available and it is only on rare occasions that ox-peckers have been seen on elephant. I have seen them twice on warthog and on both occasions the pig stood perfectly still and enjoyed allowing birds to search for parasites, turning the head slowly from side to side so that they could get at the creases in the neck. J. E. Hughes (*Eighteen Years on Lake Bengweula*) says: 'The tick-bird follows warthog who take little notice; they busy themselves finding ticks all round the anus.' They have been recorded on galloping kudu and I have seen them on trotting rhinoceros on many occasions. I have never seen them on giraffe or waterbuck though a flock of red-billed flew round a herd of the former but, after inspection, failed to alight. But Mr E. Davison (in litt.) of the Wankie Game Reserve says: 'The yellow-bill seem particularly fond of giraffe and several have been noted with every troop. Frequently, when a giraffe bends down to drink, the ox-peckers will enter its anus; five giraffe have been seen drinking in a row, each with an ox-pecker in the anus; the first action when the giraffe stops drinking is to shake the head vigorously and dislodge the birds, which make no attempt to enter the anus again until the giraffe drinks again; just what the birds are after is not understood.'

Neuman records a single bird riding on a great bustard (*kori*). Camels ignore them. Zebra dislike them and on one occasion in Rhodesia they caused a stampede. Horses will sometimes tolerate them whilst on other occasions resent them. Donkeys resent them and have been seen to roll or run under bushes to rid themselves of the birds. I have often seen both species near ostrich but no attempt to ride. I have seen yellow-billed resting on a basking crocodile without any indication of feeding or of alarming the reptile at my approach.

Warning game

When at rest in a tree or when drinking both species are remarkably tame. On two occasions I have had both red and yellow-billed resting and preening in a tree close to chattering humans eating their lunch. They are very different birds when on wild game.

There is no question about the fact that they warn game on the approach of man. Their first reaction to man is to creep round to the safe side of the animal on which they ride, behind an ear or the tail, but keeping an eye on the intruder; then if one continues to approach they will all fly up, often in a circle, uttering a harsh scolding note. On two occasions, after shooting eland and rhinoceros, they have circled round swearing at me. On another occasion I was stalking a leopard which was in turn stalking an oribi; on the oribi were three ox-peckers; on seeing me they at once flew in my direction calling loudly and then proceeded to mob the leopard. The oribi, of course, made off at once.

When feeding on domestic stock they sometimes try and warn them if a man approaches but more often do not do so. They may have learned that domestic stock pays no attention to their warning call or they may have learned that animals accompanied by a herdsman do not need a warning.

At Nanyuki I once approached a captive Grevy's zebra, very tame and gentle. He had seven yellow-billed birds on him; as I approached they rose and yelled; this threw the zebra, who normally would come for sugar, into a panic and he raced round his enclosure as though the devil were after him, and it took a considerable time before he quietened down and came to my hand. This beast had been caught as a foal and had been over a year in captivity.

I think there is no question about wild game being conscious of an extra protection when accompanied by *Buphagus*. A rhinoceros is much more alert when without *Buphagus* than when they accompany him. I have noted this especially with buffalo and eland. But *Buphagus* knows the range of a shot-gun, not of a rifle, and will seldom fly off hissing and swearing until one is about eighty yards from him. It is consequently easier to stalk game when accompanied by *Buphagus* on whom they rely for advanced information of danger and relax in consequence, than to stalk game unaccompanied by *Buphagus* and therefore more on the alert.

Between Marsabit and Isiolo in Kenya I saw three yellow-billed flying over two cheetah who were clearly annoyed; the cheetah were on the move and when the birds came too near, one of the cheetah jumped up trying to strike the bird. As the birds were calling loudly and had seen me—which the cheetah had not—I am uncertain whether the birds' aim was a warning or a wish to search the cheetah.

About twenty miles west of Marsabit I witnessed seven wild dogs chasing a female gerenuk and above the dogs flew eight yellow-billed, calling loudly and angrily. Unfortunately the country was too rough to enable me to follow, but I imagined that the birds were angry with the dogs for chasing a friend.

In 1908 I was stalking a greater kudu in Nyasaland in thick bush. He was browsing and had a small party of ox-peckers on him, which gave him complete security and confidence. When I was within about sixty yards of him one of the birds, whilst inspecting one of the huge ears, must have suspected something, for he stood motionless with head erect; he took wing and flew towards me, recognising me as a potential predator. He screamed and flew back to the kudu; up went the kudu's head and off he slunk, soon lost to sight.

Movement

Both species, when alighting on an animal, will usually make the initial perch on the back or rump, sometimes, like a woodpecker, on a fore or hind leg. Their claws are exceedingly sharp and have a peculiar knack of adhering to hair or wool; when on a beast they can move up, sideways, and down with equal ease.

The red-billed perches freely on trees, sometimes for considerable periods to preen and digest. They will occasionally rest on animals and will sometimes splay themselves out as though 'anting,' trying to expose as much surface of the body as possible in contact with the hide of the animal. On the ground they both walk and hop. I have never seen the yellow-billed on trees, but they no doubt use trees for similar purposes as the red-billed.

It is significant that the tail feathers of *Buphagus* are soft and rounded when

211

freshly moulted but soon wear to a stiffness comparable to the texture of the woodpeckers'; the tail is definitely used as a support when climbing about a beast.

Roosting

A flock of red-billed roosted regularly in the thatch of my hut at Nyeri; they would arrive about sundown and after a good preen would enter small cavities; they would all fly out together about half an hour after sun-up and go straight for a rhinoceros of which there were always some in view in those days (1902–3). In Somaliland I was camped near a broad sandy river bed where masses of camels were tethered for the night. These were always accompanied by a large flock of red-billed. After dark I went out with a torch and found many roosting on humps with heads well tucked in under scapulars. It was a very cold night.

Large communal roosts are not uncommon. I have come across them in both Kenya and Rhodesia. In the latter country we located a herd of about 200 buffalo which could always be found in more or less the same locality. This herd was attended by large numbers of both species of *Buphagus*. The yellow-billed formed a communal roost in some low bush, coming in by small parties and diving in much as starlings do; their numbers approached 80 to 100 birds. The red-billed no doubt had their own roost but I never located it.

Nesting

In 1903 a pair of red-billed nested in the thatch of my hut at Nyeri. The nest was an untidy structure of hairs, twigs and grass; hairs were seen to be taken from both mules and donkeys, and are deliberately pulled out much to the annoyance of beasts. But they usually nest in old timber in Kenya, and in Natal often under the roofs of houses.

The yellow-billed is said to nest more often in rock crevices than in tree holes. A nest found in Nyasaland was in a tree hole, when parents were feeding young.

Stark (*Fauna S. Afr.*, I, p. 21), in referring to hairs pulled from a donkey's coat, says: 'in collecting these, the birds showed a certain amount of ingenuity, the individual hairs as they were pulled out being placed end to end on the donkey's back until neat bundles were accumulated, as large as they could conveniently carry; these were then carried to the nest under the roof of a house.'

Both species, so far as two observations go, feed their young on caterpillars and grasshoppers. It is a curious fact that even in the breeding season both species retain the small-flock habit. At Nyeri the red-billed could often be seen in the breeding season hopping about on the ground searching for nursery food, as many as eight or ten birds together, each parent as it finds food flying off to the nest and returning to the small flock after feeding the chicks.

In *Bokmakerei*, Aug. 1951, p. 72, is an account of a juvenile yellow-bill whose stomach contents contained 'a few skins of cattle ticks, five pieces of quartz, two pieces of sandstone, one piece of shale and three pieces of siliceous rock . . . apparently, as the skins of tick, their main diet, are tough, these chippings are necessary for digestion.'

Capture

Mr Raymond Hook of Nanyuki tells me they can be easily caught by placing a skeleton harness on a horse or cow and attaching many horse-hair nooses to the harness.

Edibility

Van Someren records that cats will not eat the red-billed. I can confirm this in two instances. My cat killed a red-billed chick, almost ready to fly, at Nyeri and would not eat it; and at Fort Hall I tempted a tame serval cat with a dead adult red-billed and it was refused; but both my domestic cat and serval scarcely knew what hunger was.

Intelligence, flocking and competition

The yellow-billed is generally a stupider and tamer bird than the red-billed. I have only once seen them flock with another bird, and then on the ground with a party of wattled starlings (*Creatophora*), searching for grasshoppers.

Yellow-billed are usually in larger flocks, from ten to fifty.

The two species rarely consort together. Near Nanyuki I have seen both species among domestic cattle but keeping strictly apart and not paying much attention to each other; but on another occasion, also on domestic cattle, I saw a flock of over thirty yellow-billed chase away about a dozen red-billed and drive them right off the herd before returning to their beasts. But whenever I have seen them near each other there is restlessness, excitement a nd some scolding.

The following incident shows intelligence. In June 1902 I was on the Athi Plains near Nairobi far from trees of any sort, and came across a herd of eland grazing near a herd of Masai cattle. On the eland was a small party of yellow-billed *Buphagus*. As I approached the eland, the birds flew off screaming towards the Masai cattle. In mid-flight a lanner falcon stooped and missed. The birds at once turned and flew back to the eland, concentrating on the old bull, under whose belly they took refuge, though the beast was on the move, the lanner hovering quite close to the beast for a minute or so, but the ox-peckers were safe and silent and remained in their security for some time after the lanner had given up the chase and departed.

Works consulted

Moreau, E., 'Food of *Buphagus erythrorhynchus*,' *Bull. Ent. Res.*, XXIV (1933), pp. 325-35.
Jackson, F. J., *Birds of Kenya and Uganda*, III, 1938.
Van Someren, 'The Red-billed Ox-pecker and its Relation to Stock in Kenya,' *E. Afr. Agric. Journ.*, XVII (1951), pp. 1-11.
Pitman, C. R. S., 'Ox-peckers,' *Zoo Life*, Spring 1956.

BIRDS MAKING USE OF OTHER BIRDS

For transport

THE carriage of birds on the backs of mammals and other birds, and the frequent habit of chicks sheltering in the plumage or under the wings of their parents and the unquestioned habit of many parents carrying their young, demonstrate that some birds do indeed make use of others for protection, for food and for transportation. It is, therefore, not impossible that certain small birds take advantage of the passage of larger birds for transportation. To dismiss such a possibility as incredible would entail brushing aside a whole mass of circumstantial evidence, some of which must surely be based on fact.

In the *Zoologist*, 1881, p. 260, is an editorial note which asks for confirmation of a passage in a book by Dr van Lennep—*Bible Customs in Bible Lands*—in which it is affirmed that cranes habitually assist small migrants across the Mediterranean; no details are given, nor authorities, and the whole statement seems to be most unconvincing. But in the *Zoologist*, 1882, p. 78, T. H. Nelson records that a Mr Wilson of South Gare Breakwater at the mouth of the Tees noted a short-eared owl arriving across the sea on the morning of 16 October. The bird alighted but ten yards from Mr Wilson, who then saw a small bird emerge from the owl's back. This small bird was subsequently caught and proved to be a goldcrest.

In the *Field* of 15 September 1945 occurred an article by Frank W. Lane which gives many recorded instances of the transportation of small birds by large. As Mr Lane's article may not be readily available to everyone, I give a short summary of it.

Several North American Indian tribes believe the pick-a-back story. Egyptians had a belief that small birds were carried by larger ones, mainly storks and cranes. A correspondent writing from Crete in 1880 saw small birds leave crane when fired at. A Swede in the island of Rhodes saw some small birds leave the back of some stork after they had come to ground. Hagland in 1919 in Alberta records having heard much twittering from a flock of cranes as they passed overhead without seeing any small birds. The twittering came and went with the cranes. In November 1936 a St Louis journal alleged that a humming bird was found in the feathers of a Canada goose after the latter had been shot. Again, in *Time and Tide* of 9 December 1939 David Haig Thomas records that he found a goldcrest clinging to the feathers of a short-eared owl which he shot after passing over the North Sea. The subject cannot be summarily dismissed on this evidence.

Three further cases have come to my notice. When I was visiting the Spurn Head Lighthouse in the autumn of 1929 the keeper gave me a dead short-eared owl and two goldcrests which had struck the light the previous evening. They all lay dead together on the lighthouse balcony, and had struck at the same moment.

The second case was related to me by a naval officer who had done much convoy work to Russia in 1943 and 1944. A flock of swan passed over his craft and he fired at them with his shot-gun. The report of his gun disturbed 'quite a lot of small black and white birds which had been travelling in the swans' plumage; they came fluttering out and were last seen following the swans and trying to remount but failed to do so as the swans' flight was more rapid than that of the small birds.'

I asked if there could be any doubt about feathers being mistaken for birds and was assured that the small birds were seen to follow the swans until out of sight; feathers would have slowly drifted downwards.

The third case. At the Ushant Light and again at Tarbatness Light both owls and goldcrests have struck the lantern at the same moment, and at Killantringan Light I have a record of a goldcrest striking the lantern at the same moment as a corncrake (*Crex*). It is a remarkable coincidence that these birds should have struck and been killed on impact if there was not some form of close association.

I find it difficult to comment on this alleged habit; I cannot disbelieve it; I cannot accept it without proof of a more direct and definite nature.

For nest-building

Edward Grey in his *Charm of Birds* relates how he had observed long-tailed tits (*Aegithalos*) settling on turkeys' backs to collect feathers for their nests and I have seen both the house sparrow (*Passer domesticus*) and the nuthatch (*Sitta europaea*) removing feathers from a living chicken for a similar purpose.

House sparrows have been recorded attacking woodpigeons in London with the object of obtaining feathers for nesting material, on one occasion securing seven feathers after a vicious peck. The chasing of both woodpigeons and domesticated rock pigeon in my London garden by house sparrows has been frequently noted, often accompanied by close-contact attack. In Wiltshire I have seen a house sparrow chase a turtle dove and obtain a feather.

In Somaliland I have seen weavers bullying and harrying a dove (*Streptopelia senegalensis*), not letting it rest until a feather was dropped; this was then picked up and the chase ceased.

For food

In both Africa and India I have noted the habit of parrots and bulbuls, when eating figs, being attended by species of sunbird (*Nectarinidae*). The parrots and bulbuls break up the fig, which is then left for the sunbirds to suck and extract the juices. A rather similar habit has been noted between waxwings (*Bombycilla*) and redpolls (*Carduelis linaria*) in winter in Arctic Finland. The waxwings would sit quietly munching the fruit of rowan (*Pyrus aucuparia*) whilst the redpolls would collect under the tree and eat the discarded seeds and pulp. If the waxwings moved, the redpolls would follow them. I have seen bullfinches (*Pyrrhula*) attending flocks of redwings (*Turdus musicus*) in Wiltshire, the former feeding on the ground and eating the debris of berries dropped by the latter. Hawfinches (*Coccothraustes*) will accompany flocks of fieldfares (*Turdus pilaris*) and redwings in order to feed on the kernels of hawthorn which the latter drop from the bushes in which they feed.

Bates (*Journ. Bombay N.H. Soc.*, 1952, p. 941) and Biddulph (*op. cit.*, 1954, p. 209) record an association between a drongo and the yellow-naped wood-pecker in India, the former only interested in insects disturbed by the wood-pecker and the latter only interested in grubs and non-flying insect life.

Hirundines will often attend flocks of feeding starlings, catching insects disturbed by them, and I have noted both *Hirundo* and *Riparia* attending the huge flocks of migrating wagtails at Entebbe on the Victoria Nyanza and in the Fayoum. I have also seen swallows in Africa (species unknown) attending bustard (*Ardeotis*) and catching disturbed insects. In Africa swallows and bee-eaters profit by following bulbuls and feeding on insects disturbed by the latter.

The carmine bee-eater (*Merops nubicus*) has been observed riding on an Abdim's stork, profiting by insects disturbed by the bird when feeding.

The American wigeon (*A. americana*) attends coot to profit by the weeds pulled up by the latter. Wigeon (*Anas penelope*) are often found with brent geese (*Branta bernicla*), the latter profiting by the scraps of zostera pulled up by the geese.

The sheathbill (*Chionis*) attends the 'rookeries' of both penguins and seals in the Antarctic, profiting by the parasitic worms in the faeces of the former and the afterbirth of the latter.

The familiar case of vultures watching each other when soaring is well known; so that if one bird spies a carcase and drops to it, the others, seeing the drop, also converge, until the vultures over a vast area are drawn to the feast. In the early days of Kenya when the game abounded and carcases were plenti-ful—mostly kills by lion—one would be quite unconscious of vultures in the heavens unless one used glasses; then at infinite height one could discover small specks soaring this way and that; and then, as if on a given signal, all would glide or drop in the same direction.

I shot a hartebeeste near Nairobi on a brilliantly clear day and took great pains to discover the moment when vultures paid attention to my beast. There were four vultures in view, at a great height, at the moment of gralloching; their reaction was not noticeable until I had moved away some 300 yards, where I sat with binoculars; I had left the whole carcase intact except for the two hind legs and the saddle and the raw red meat was displayed at its best, for I desired to attract the vultures' attention. At exactly seventeen minutes after I left the carcase a single vulture came swishing down from the heavens and alighted about twenty-five yards from the carcase; on looking up I could then see birds planing down from all directions, some mere specks in the sky, others half-way down; after another ten minutes there were seventeen vultures on the ground, some walking towards the carcase slowly and clearly suspicious. No bird commenced to feed until I had left the carcase for forty-two minutes and then all fell to with a will with vultures still coming down from all directions; the latest arrivals must have come immense distances, drawn by seeing others descending.

I repeated this experiment on several occasions with much the same results as regards timing and numbers. I estimated that at any given moment there was one vulture soaring to about every four to five square miles.

Both jackal and hyaena have learned the vultures' trick and watch the birds; when they see them descending they will hurry towards the line of drop; on one occasion I spied a jackal actually lying on its back on the Athi Plains and when he saw vultures dropping to a hartebeeste I had shot, off he galloped with a frequent look up to ensure he was on the correct line.

Sea birds also watch each other's flight movements, converging from long distances to places where food is abundant.

Hawks, storks and the crow family will watch each other for indications of thermal currents, especially when on migration. See also Mackintosh, *Ibis*, 1949, pp. 55-9, and Goodwin, *Ibis*, 1949, pp. 59-63.

For protection or convenience

I am by no means convinced that some birds nest in the nests of larger birds or near the nests of larger birds, purely for protection. It may be entirely incidental, the smaller or weaker bird finding the location convenient.

In the Jordan Valley I have found the Spanish sparrow (*P. hispaniolensis*) breeding in the nests of the larger Raptores.

The house sparrow (*P. domesticus*) has bred in the nests of heron (*Ardea*), stork (*Ciconia alba*), house martin (*Delichon*)—a clear case of eviction—and magpie (*Pica*). The case of the sparrow and house martin is particularly mean, for the former deliberately evicts the builder and owner, after the manner of some of our Borough Councils, without compensation; and the sparrow shows particular cunning in waiting until the martin has lined its nest with soft feathers before he takes possession.

I know many cases of jackdaws (*C. monedula*) breeding in holes in trees above which was a large rookery. At my old home at Mottisfont in a single tree were three herons' nests, a green woodpecker's (*Picus viridis*) nest and at the base of the tree a mallard (*Anas platyrhynchus*) had its nest. In this latter case the heron at once attacked a carrion crow which had designs on the mallard's eggs.

Robson (*Brit. B.*, 1955, p. 189) records two cases of tree sparrows (*Passer montanus*) nesting in buzzards' nests.

Mountfort (*epist.*) records both jackdaws (*Corvus monedula*) and Spanish sparrows (*Passer hispaniolensis*) nesting in the foundations of the nest of the white stork (*Ciconia ciconia*).

Both wrens and sparrows will roost in and occupy house martins' nests for breeding. In Morocco a colony of white-rumped swift (*Apus affinis*) failed completely to occupy their own nests in face of sparrow intrusion. In the *Field* (13 Sept. 1952) is recorded the case of house martins building in a trespassing sparrow and starving it to death.

Leslie Brown (*Ibis*, 1955, 206) gives many cases in Kenya where several species of weaver birds (*Ploceidae*) have been found breeding in the nests of Raptores, more for convenience than protection.

Both merlin and red-backed shrike have been known to nest in fieldfare colonies, the latter protecting the former by mobbing intruders.

Verreaux's eagle-owl (*Bubo lacteus*) often breeds in the nest of the hammer-kop (*Scopus*) and has been known to do so in the nest of Wahlberg's eagle.

On the Yenesei River, Popham found nests of the red-breasted goose (*Branta ruficollis*) under bluffs occupied by buzzard and falcons, assuring the geese 'protection against marauding foxes.' But it is very doubtful if buzzard or falcons would deter a fox from raiding a goose's nest. In north-east Greenland, barnacle geese (*Branta leucopsis*) have been found nesting on ledges around the occupied nest of a Greenland falcon (*F. candicans*).

Durango (*Orn. Fenn.*, 1954, pp. 1-18) records tufted duck (*Aythya fuligula*) habitually nesting in colonies of gulls and terns. When the latter change their breeding-ground, the ducks follow; the author considers this is to the ducks' advantage as mobbing action by the gulls affords protection against predators.

In Australia gulls have been seen riding on the backs of pelican, possibly for convenience but perhaps also for piracy.

Tengmalm's owl (*Aegolius*) frequently uses the old nest of the black wood-pecker (*Dryocopus*), a clear case of convenience, as are the cases of the green sandpiper (*T. ochropus*) and wood sandpiper (*T. glareola*) using the old nests of hawks and other birds. Hobbies (*F. subbuteo*) often use the old nests of the carrion crow (*C. corone*).

The pygmy falcon (*Polihierax semitorquatus*) in Somaliland habitually uses the nests of weavers (*Dinemellia*) and the starling (*Heteropsar*); in Little Nama-qualand I found a huge conglomerate nest of the social weaver (*Philetarius*) which was being used by a pair of pygmy falcon who would enter the honey-combed structure at various places to devour their prey, to rest and preen, etc. The weavers paid no attention at all and were often in the closest contact with the little hawks, who also roosted in this strange crowded bird-slum.

It is interesting that this small falcon is infested by mallophaga belonging to a genus *Neopsittaconirmus* hitherto only found on parrots. This parasite appears to be only subspecifically distinct from that found on *Agapornis perso-nata*. Although the two host species do not occur together in British Somali-land, they overlap in other parts of their range; no mallophaga have been seen from *Polihierax* elsewhere than from British Somaliland.

Nearly all birds like company of sorts; birds attract birds; even the pug-nacious robin and the aggressive cuckoo will migrate in company; flocking gives confidence and protection, also in many cases a better chance of food. The mixed hunting party of tits and other insect-eaters in winter has many advantages to all members of the flock. I have visited the large ibis-heron-cormorant-darter communal breeding slums on islands in the Victoria Nyanza, in Rajputana, on the Lake of Antioch and elsewhere, and the immediate reaction to a threat by predators is very striking, the whole colony rising in wrath as a team and making a raid impossible. Large terneries and gulleries and the crowded cliff breeders show equally well the team reaction to a raid.

PLATE 44

Gulls riding on Pelicans [Australia]

Single pairs of any of these communal breeders could not hope to survive a raid, except in the case of the larger gulls, who can well protect their nests even against a raven.

Rothschild and Clay (*F.F. & C.*, p. 14) give several cases of this type of commensalism (quoting largely from Durango).

Durango (*Ibis*, 1949, p. 140) gives examples of some birds taking advantage of the protection afforded by communal breeders. Tufted duck, black guillemots and turnstones place their eggs, often quite openly, when nesting in colonies of gulls and terns, though normally their eggs would be well concealed in tufts of grass or under stones. Penguineries and rookeries automatically protect their eggs and young by sheer numbers. It is, therefore, not surprising that many birds seek the company of others, perhaps for protection but more likely for sociability and convenience.

The Merops–Ardeotis association

This association was first noted by Arthur Neumann in his *Elephant Hunting in East Africa* (1898, pp. 280-1, 340) where he says of his Lake Rudolph trip:

There were numbers of rose-coloured bee-eaters here and I saw one large green one ... it was here too that I observed a curious thing which later became a common sight. It is the habit of *Merops nubicus* to ride on the back of *Eupodotis kori* which is common about the north-east extremity of Bassa. It sits far back on the rump of its mount as a boy rides a donkey. The pauw does not appear to resent this liberty but stalks majestically along, whilst its brilliantly-clad little jockey keeps a look-out, sitting sideways, and now and again flies off after an insect it has espied, returning again after its chase to its 'camel.' I have never seen two bee-eaters riding on one pauw. I have also seen this bird on goats, sheep and antelope but the pauw seems its favourite steed. I imagine it gets more flights this way at game put up by its bearer, which also affords it a point of vantage whence to sight and pursue its prey in a country where suitable sticks on which to perch are few.

And again on page 340,

A rose-coloured bee-eater made use of one of a pair of black-and-white storks as a steed in the same way as I have often seen them do with the bustard; it tried the other stork who refused to be ridden.

On page 281 in the same book is an excellent illustration of bustard and bee-eater.

In *Ibis*, 1943, p. 100, Moreau, quoting Myers, records two cases from the

Sudan. Then follows an eruption. No less than nine letters on the subject in the *Ibis*. On the Zambesi I have seen *M. n. nubicoides* on sheep and cattle and on one occasion I had a whole breeding colony of these glorious birds floating around me in the sunlight and catching insects I disturbed as I walked through long grass. I soon entered into the fun and with a stick was able to add to the sport, which lasted for over an hour. In the majority of cases the victims were small grasshoppers and so close were the birds to me that I might have caught several in a butterfly net.

Between 1901 and 1905 I was stationed in Kenya and had many opportunities of seeing both *Ardeotis* and *Merops nubicus*. I never saw more than a single bird riding at a time, though I have seen a pair of *Merops* each on a single *Ardeotis*. I never saw them on ostrich but can add the warthog as a 'steed' though this was strongly resented. When riding, the *Merops* showed great alertness for movement, using the perch solely as a convenient stance and the 'steed' as a likely disturber of game. I never saw *Ardeotis* show any resentment. Rothschild and Clay (*F.F. & C.*, p. 13) record this bee-eater riding on ostriches and certain large mammals, as well as on bustard.

The frequency of this association is, I believe, correctly interpreted by North as a specific character (*Ibis*, 1944, p. 174), for as far as I am aware, it has seldom been observed with regard to other bee-eaters. I agree with Mackworth Praed (*Ibis*, 1946, p. 132) that the alleged case of a glossy starling (*Lamprocolius*) riding on an Abdim's stork (*Sphenorhynchus*) was also a carmine bee-eater.

I also believe the object to be a vantage point from which to observe food disturbed by the bustard. George Moncur (*Ibis*, 1946, p. 326) records that a bustard was seen to feed a carmine bee-eater who 'removed all or part of the insect from the bustard's beak' and that he had no doubt 'that the larger bird was feeding the smaller.' I think there is no question that a friendly relationship exists between the carmine bee-eater and bustard which appears to be entirely to the advantage of the former. But I cannot help suggesting that George Moncur might have been mistaken in his interpretation.

Brood parasitism

This concerns parasitism of the nest of one species by another species; and the consequent dependence on the host to incubate the parasite's egg or eggs.

The habit occurs in the *Icteridae* in cowbirds (*Molothrus*); [1] among cuckoos of the Old World; among some South American *Cuculidae* (*Tapera naevia*, two species of *Dromococcyx*, and *Crotophaga*); in *Indicator*, the honey-guides, who parasitise bee-eaters, barbets and woodpeckers; in some of the African weavers (*Ploceidae*); and in a single duck (*Heteronetta stricapilla*) of southern South America whose eggs have been found in the nests of other duck, geese, rails, gulls and even in that of a vulture (*Milvago*), night heron (*Nycticorax*) and swan (*Coscoroba*).

There is a huge literature on the subject and I have little to say on the subject having but small experience of it, and nothing new to add.

I would only remark that in the case of our British cuckoo, though I regard it as proved beyond doubt that in the vast majority of cases the egg is laid in the nest of the foster-parent, there is evidence which cannot be ignored that rarely the egg is deposited by the bill after having been laid on the ground or elsewhere. Photographic evidence of a cuckoo approaching the nest with an egg in her mouth may depict an isolated case of deposition, or maybe it is the egg removed from the nest of another foster-parent; but such evidence cannot be brushed aside. Nature has more than one way of doing many things.

I have not yet seen a photograph of a cuckoo actually laying its egg in another bird's nest.

There is little doubt that the sight of eggs acts as a stimulus, probably in *Heteronetta*, but especially in gallinaceous birds. In Suffolk I came across a domestic fowl which had purloined a clutch of red-legged partridge (*Alectoris rufa*) and brought them home into the farmyard, and was caring for them until they were full-grown. Then there is the case of the Norfolk Buff Orpington which laid in a pheasant's nest. The pheasant hatched the chicks, and took them into the woods where they learned to fly and would join driven birds in a covert shoot. In Hampshire, a domestic hen laid in a partridge's nest which already contained a full complement; the hen added five more but as soon as the young partridge chicks emerged, off they went with their mother, leaving the hen's eggs to rot. There is also a record of a nest containing pheasant's, grey partridge and red-legged partridge's eggs. Pheasants are notoriously fond of laying their eggs in the nests of other birds. In the

[1] A remarkable case of *Molothrus ater* laying two eggs in each of two near-by nests of Wilson's Phalarope is recorded by Trowbridge (*Auk*, 1939; p. 77).

duck-ground at Mottisfont, where many mallard bred alongside pheasants, it was more a rule than an exception to find odd pheasants' eggs in mallards' nests.

Whenever many species of duck congregate for breeding, such as Myvatn in Iceland or in the marshes of Manitoba, it is not uncommon for the egg-stimulus to induce indiscriminate laying.

BIRDS MAKING USE OF REPTILES

The Pluvianus–Crocodile association

THE Egyptian plover (*Pluvianus*) and the spur-winged plover (*Hoplopterus*) have developed the habit of attending crocodiles and feeding on either leeches or debris between the teeth. Herodotus mentions it and Brehm stated it as a fact though he had never observed it. Flower never observed it and doubted it, whilst A. L. Butler, whose opportunities in the Sudan were combined with remarkable observational power, could not support the claim that *Pluvianus* entered the mouths of crocodiles and picked their teeth. Moreau (*Ibis*, 1944, p. 410) refers to my statement in my *Birds of Egypt* where I say: 'The Egyptian plover is one of the many "Crocodile Birds" which enter the mouth of the gaping amphibian and clean its teeth, extracting lice and other vermin,' and remarks that the old story probably still rests with Herodotus and lacks confirmation. In *Ibis*, 1944, p. 410, North quotes Moreau as saying: 'Meinertzhagen's reference to the habit of the Egyptian plover entering the mouth of the crocodile and extracting lice etc. has not been confirmed by modern authorities,' and again, 'perhaps the old story rests solely on Herodotus.' I was perhaps to blame for not adding relevant evidence but I do not make statements of fact resting solely on evidence over 2,000 years old.

North of Khartoum I watched a large crocodile emerge from the river on to a sand-bank, flop down on its belly, close its eyes and open its jaws. Three *Pluvianus* who had been feeding near by at once flew to it, one perching on the outer gums and pecking at the teeth, the other two remaining on the ground and inspecting the mouth, occasionally reaching up and pecking the teeth; I could not say what was extracted by the birds but the whole episode looked as though the crocodile expected and invited the birds, and that the birds were quite at home inspecting the inside of the mouth of the crocodile.

I also have a letter from Peter Haig Thomas dated March 1950 in which he says: 'I saw Egyptian plover enter the mouth of a crocodile several times and pick its teeth. The most interesting case was that of a crocodile 10-12 feet long, who was lying half out of the water on shingle with his mouth shut. On the approach of the plover he very slowly opened his mouth and the plover ran in and was certainly most of the time inside the mouth, thoroughly picking the teeth on both sides of the lower jaw.'

I was on the Kafue River in north-west Rhodesia in 1907 and watched crocodiles coming out to a sand-bank within a few yards of me; many came out and the procedure was in every case identical. No sooner on dry land than they would flop down, shut their eyes and open their mouths wide. The spur-winged plover (*Hoplopterus armatus*) would come flying in, sometimes from a long distance, and at once run up to the open jaws and pick teeth, though I never saw a bird actually enter the jaws.

It has also been suggested that the spur-winged plover serve to warn crocodiles of danger, while the bird profits from the partnership by feeding on insects at the basking ground in addition to removing parasites and debris from the crocodile's mouth.

Both spur-winged plovers (*armatus* and *spinosus*) and the water dikkop (*Burhinus vermiculatus*), and on the Gold Coast some egret ('pure white ospreys') are recorded as picking the teeth of a crocodile (*Field*, 25 July 1957).

For convenience

I have seen the tick-bird (*Buphagus erythorhynchus*) on the back of a crocodile without attempting to search for food.

On Flat Island near Mauritius I have seen a sentinel whimbrel (*Numenius phaeopus*) standing on the back of a giant land tortoise, while the remainder of the flock fed on the shore close by. Barbour (*Naturalist at Large*, 1943, p. 65) records gulls standing on marine turtles off Nicaragua. Lack (*Ibis*, 1944, p. 222) records gulls, probably L. *atricilla*, on large marine turtles off the west coast of Mexico, adding that the number of bird droppings on the back of the turtle probably indicates frequency of this habit. In Nyasaland, Uganda and the Sudan, wagtails have seen been resting on crocodiles, also the Egyptian goose (*Alopochen*), the tree-duck (*Dendrocygna fulva*), the cattle egret (*Ardeola ibis*), the pied kingfisher (*Ceryle rudis*), the little cormorant (*P. africanus*) and the darter (*Anhinga*). In the case of the kingfisher and cormorant, the back of the reptile was being used as a convenient perch from which to sally out and fish.

Use of snakes' skins in birds' nests

Rand (*Chicago Acad. Sci. Nat. Hist. Misc.*, No. 125, 1953) cites many cases of birds, mostly Passerines, in whose nests shed snakes' skins have been found and concludes that it is the natural outcome of the tendency to use any suitable material available and not as a protective warning.

I have on two occasions found bits of snake-skin in birds' nests, once in Sinai when a small piece of skin was woven into the nest of the rufous warbler (*Agrobates*) and once at Magadi in Kenya, when a small piece of snake-skin lay at the bottom of the nest of the small plover (*venustus*) mingled with small pebbles.

BIRDS MAKING USE OF FISH

MURPHY (*Oceanic B. of S. America:* p. 1245) records the frigate bird (*Fregata*) and the bonito co-operating against flying fish, the latter making them fly when they are harried by the bird. Ridley (*Ibis*, 1954, p. 311) records white-winged black tern (*Chlidonias leucoptera*) on Lake Rudolph following tiger-fish (*Hydrocyon*) and catching small fry trying to escape from them. The tern would hover within a few inches of the surface, catching the fry in mid-air.

REPTILES ATTENDANT ON BIRDS

ON several occasions I have visited the large breeding colonies of water birds (*Plegadis*, *Phalacrocorax*, *Anhinga*, *Threskiornis*, etc.) breeding on islands on the Victoria Nyanza and on every occasion I have found python moving about stealthily among the nests on the tree-tops. I have shot five of such snakes and on every occasion the reptile contained the young of one or other breeding bird, on one occasion three baby *Anhinga*. These snakes must have swum over from the mainland and have probably become parasitic on bird-colonies.

The association of rattlesnakes with the American burrowing owl (*Athene cunicularia*) and prairie-dog is well known. This unnatural association has been induced by a common interest—an underground home. No doubt the snakes eat the young owls and owls' eggs; no doubt the owls eat the young prairie-dogs and perhaps young snakes and no doubt the prairie-dogs are a perfect nuisance to snakes and owls as they scurry about the burrows; but all the same the association lives at apparent ease. It is significant that crowded prairie-dog burrows have few owls and crowded owl burrows have few prairie-dogs. And rattlesnakes are the exception, not the rule.

INDEX